# PEOPLE OF THE

*George with two grandchildren before a walk.*

# PEOPLE OF
# THE CENTURY

## Gwendolen Freeman

BREWIN BOOKS

First Published by Brewin Books Ltd
Studley, Warwickshire. B80 7LG
in April 1999

British Library Cataloguing In Publication Data.
A catalogue record for this book is available
from The British Library

ISBN 1 85858 134 6

Typeset in Baskerville.
Made and printed in Great Britain by
SupaPrint (Redditch) Ltd

By the same author:


The Houses Behind (Allen & Unwin 1947)

Children Never Tell (Allen & Unwin 1949)

When You Are Old (Allen & Unwin 1951)

The Last Kings of Thule - a translation of the
French book by Jean Malaurie (Allen & Unwin 1956)

Between Two Worlds - a book of verse (Outposts 1978)

The Leavises - The first essay (Cambridge University Press 1984)

A Zeppelin in My Childhood (Charles Skilton 1989)

United Family Record - Some Late Victorians (Brewin Books 1989)

World of an Artist - A Life of William Freeman (Brewin Books 1990)

Alma Mater (Girton College 1990)

Scriptural Beasts (Charles Skilton 1991)

Ways of Loving (Brewin Books 1993)

Flora at School (Ergon Press 1994)

The Dodona Oak (Brewin Books 1995)

Anna with Tristram (Brewin Books 1995)

Midland Thirties (Brewin Books 1998)

# CONTENTS

# CHAPTER 1

# People of the Century

Historians are not scientists. They do not issue neutral statements. They select and have opinions, especially if they are writing of recent times. If you have lived long enough for your experience to become part of recorded history, you may feel indignant and protest, "This is not true".

We may indeed get more of a feeling for the history of a period by studying individual lives. Television has discovered this, but has given witnesses only a few minutes. It is also set on soiling reputations. There is a monotonous similarity in TV muck-raking of the lives of the "great".

In a long life I have met many people, including the humble. Now I have picked out a collection of lives, shaping them a little and altering names so that they shall not be recognised. Like the historians I have used them to represent tendencies, but I have kept closely to detail. They all illustrate some aspect of the century.

CHAPTER 2

# Despoiling the Countryside and Loving Jesus

The small semi-detached house is still there though it must have been much altered. It was built at the turn of the century in a quiet road on the borders of Surbiton - the Thames-side settlement that had grown up with the South Western Railway. With its good steam-train services it had attracted a colony of London businessmen and was becoming a symbol of middle-class snobbery, but George, Rosetta and their three daughters claimed distinction only from the local church and school. Their road still had a wood and scraps of field behind it and gaps where houses were still to be built. Along it went a little horses-traffic and a few bicycles.

The gaps between houses were filled long ago, and the gardens are old enough to display flowering trees and birches. Cars rush along the road from a thoroughfare with shops to a junction of five ways, and a bulge has been made in the pavement to prevent motorists from speeding out.

The solid dark green gate bore the name "Vellmead", but where the name came from we did not ask. At the time suburban houses had names, not numbers, and a good deal of invention went into them – from the names of honeymoon places to humour as in "Dunroamin". But to us "Vellmead" had only one association – the home of our grandparents.

The front garden had a small well-cut lawn and a line of neat rose-trees  beside the gravel path. The path led to a step – always whitened by hand in those days – and a dark green front door. But we went through a latticework gate at the side to the scullery door and our small fluttering grandmother in a grey flannel blouse and long skirt. Beyond was the back garden with another small lawn, two apple trees, a rose-bed with exquisite low blooms and an arch. There were also sweet red gooseberries, and long stems of rhubarb growing surprisingly next to the dustbin.

The house had no electricity or gas. An oil lamp hung from the

2

hall ceiling and glowing table lamps lighted the downstairs rooms. The cleaning, filling and lighting of the lamps were important duties, and candles were used upstairs. Their little circles of gold gave the children a feeling of mystery and melancholy. Downstairs were coal fires, not lighted every day, with their polished brass and iron hearth furniture, and the kitchen had a long black range which cooked as well as heated. There may have been hearths upstairs, but they remained cold.

George and Rosetta were almost untouched by the arts and crafts movement of the time. Their furnishings were homely Victorian with an ecclesiastical slant. A large aspidistra stood in the front window, and the mantelpiece had a pair of white shiny pug dogs. The book-shelves in the corner entertained us with a copious children's annual named "Little Folks" with moral stories, incidents from royal families of Europe, verse, riddles and pictures. Later we dipped into the domestic novels of the time, collected by the daughters of the family, including the sweet Rosa Nouchette Carey. The only violence and crime on the shelves were in the fat black Bible.

The drawing-room, used only for visitors and festivities, was more elegant, dominated by a yellow fringed silken sofa. As in almost all middle-class homes of the time it had a piano with, above it, a print, taken from some Victorian painting, of Ruth and Naomi in the corn-field. We were more at ease in the kitchen with its faint smell of apples and of the two cats, Kitty and Darkie – an innocent name which would be impossible today.

A rag rug (bits of cloth hooked into sacking), which we considered vulgar, lay before the hearth with its black shiny range, but the well-scrubbed kitchen table gave a feeling of cleanliness; and by it was George's big wooden armchair. On the wall hung a church calendar. The one I remember best was of a pretty little dark-haired infant Samuel in a white nightgown – kneeling and praying with his hands together. On the sills outside in summer were rich petunias or fuch-sias. They went into an unused bedroom in winter. There were no small greenhouses for humble gardeners in those days.

We occasionally penetrated reverently into the big front bedroom. What chiefly impressed us was portraits of clergy on the walls, includ-ing Rosetta's hero, Arthur Winnington-Ingram, Bishop of London. He was accompanied by a coloured print of Jesus, also in a white

3

nightgown, handsomely brown-bearded and spreading out arms of blessing against rays of light. Saintly clergy and the Saviour were great comforts to Rosetta.

The family moved into "Vellmead" in 1902. This was a relief to the eldest daughter, Lucy, a pupil-teacher at the large local girls' school. She confessed later that their previous address in a side street caused her much embarrassment, as the street was considered "common". "Common" was a favourite word of the time.

George was once described ironically by an acquaintance as " a worthy citizen". He was intensely respectable and rather taciturn. A country boy from the Yorkshire-Nottingham border, born in 1845, he may have exemplified the Victorian drift to towns, for agriculture was having a hard time. At any rate he moved to London as an assistant in a draper's shop and a Sunday-school teacher. But then he was struck by tragedy.

One would hardly have expected a disaster of love in that later spare stern little man with a well-trimmed white beard. But there were many tragedies of the kind in the Victorian period with its killing diseases attacking the young. George became engaged to Miss Lucy, the draper's daughter, but then she pined away and died of "consumption". After that he remained single till he was over thirty.

But he continued to teach in Sunday school, not having lost his faith in the Lord, and there he met the small frail Rosetta, another teacher, who came from a pious family whose father was a local preacher. George proposed to Rosetta, but told her that his dead sweetheart would always come first with him. Rosetta naturally hesitated and herself became ill, but after several years accepted him. But he called his first daughter Lucy.

He left London to run his own drapery business, but he was not clever at making money and he may well, as was the practice of religious men in those days, have given a tenth of his income to the Church. Two other girls were born – but at long intervals because of Rosetta's frailty – and the family remained poor and George a fish out of water. He was released through family snobbery.

Rosetta's sister Annie had married a successful businessman in the City. They wanted to settle near Surbiton but could not do it, they said, if the brother-in-law was "in trade". So the businessman offered George a place in his office, and George became a "commuter" –

though the word was not yet invented – and travelled to London each day by the frequent steam trains which took a swarm of businessmen up and down. He was a tough little man and continued at the London office till he was over eighty and had a road accident.

But when the family moved to "Vellmead" he was not yet sixty and had two hobbies – gardening and the Church of England. Near the end of his road stood the imposing St. Matthew's with its spire, one of several Victorian churches built in a growing neighbourhood. St. Matthew's had a "low" type of service which suited George though not so much Rosetta, and on Sunday the family attended services morning and evening, with Sunday school in between for the girls.

The grandchildren were subjected to morning service at an early age, and felt almost as if St. Matthew's belonged to George. He became most conspicuous during the last hymn when he would quietly leave his place and reappear at the top of the aisle with a dark blue velvet bag on handles. He presented it politely to the first pew, and the worshippers solemnly passed it along, slipping in silver and coppers, and then offering it to the pew behind which repeated the action till the bag got back to George. Presently it reached the family pew, and the children, making no sign that they knew George, dropped in their pennies, and he continued down the lines. At the bottom of the aisle he fell in beside another reverent gentleman, and two or three more joined them, and the black-coated elderly men of God paced up the aisle to the chancel steps where the vicar waited to offer the chinking contents of the velvet bags to God. The children were proud of both George and the pennies that they had contributed.

George, besides being a sidesman, had another sign of eminence. He carried to church a thick black book which might have been entitled "Guide to the C. of E." If had all kinds of services including marriage and "the burial of the dead." It had the Litany and ceremonies of which we had never heard, the Psalms, lessons for every Sunday in the year and finally hymns ancient and modern. At services George would open the book, gesture to the child beside him to share it, and when the lessons arrived and the congregation settled comfortably and the vicar strode to the lectern, George would have his book open and point, and the child would have to read with him. There seemed something faintly irreligious in this monitoring and noticing when the vicar pronounced a word oddly or missed out a bit, but it made us superior to the rest of the congregation

In the hymns George sang out heartily in his deep voice, but when his grandchild tried to sing heartily too she was told not to make so much noise. But she knew by that time that there was one rule for children and another for grown-ups.

However, the family mingled quite well in "Good King Wenceslas" on Christmas Day. George sang solo a gruff Wenceslas while the children piped the rest, and their mother plonked away on the piano.

Surbiton had the Thames to the north, with only ferries crossing it. So if people wanted a walk they had to follow its banks or turn south up the hills which finally led to the Downs. The main road past George's modest thoroughfare went south up to the open country-side, with cottages and small shops here and there and then large estates, fields and woods.

The Thames-side people went out into the countryside and rifled it. They went on bicycle and foot, and even children walked two or three miles in the blackberry season, sometimes taking refreshments. A girl of seventeen wrote in her diary of 1902 of several blackberry excursions of half a day. Once it rained but the two girls went on picking and then tramped three miles home, arriving "soaked". Sometimes so many pickers had been to favourite places that no berries were left.

But it was not only for blackberries that families made expeditions. The girl's mother, a strong-minded woman who dabbled in author-ship, wrote, rather self-righteously, of a spring Sunday when her fam-ily of six had a picnic in a primrose wood. After the meal they filled every receptacle they had, and still, the mother reported, almost with disapproval, there were primroses left. She ended on a moral note. Some people might criticise them for not going to church on a Sunday, but surely a day admiring God's handiwork was well-spent. If she had been told that she was spoiling God's handiwork she would not have believed it.

It never occurred to people at the beginning of the century that wild flowers should be left to bloom and seed. A walk without pick-ing flowers would have been unthinkable. George was of this generation, and he had the same attitude to the country, and passed it on to his grandchildren. As they grew old enough to go for walks he would appear at their back door on Sunday afternoons between church services, and the children would be sent upstairs from the dinner-table to put on hats, coats and gloves. We would start out on a walk which was nearly always too long and tired us out. But we did not complain to him, though we moaned to our mother, as children were expected to bear the yoke. However, we fortified ourselves as we went out at the gate with the unvarying question, "Shall we find any flowers today?"

Winter walks were boring but blessedly shorter. In spring the search began again. I remember wondering if the emerald-green sprays of cow-parsley in the banks were worth picking. But no. They were only leaves, and we wanted flowers. Sometimes in February you could find a pink dead-nettle with its sweet pungent scent, but the search really began with celandines.

George was a countryman. He amazed us by being able to distinguish one tree species from another when they were leafless. He was careful about shutting gates and keeping to field paths at hay or harvest time. He knew about nuts and berries you could eat, hooking down blackberry trails with his invariable walking-stick and picking up and peeling tiny sharp beech nuts. Yet he had no idea that wild plants should be protected.

He led us to the corner of a churchyard where the first celandines appeared, and we picked them all. He took us to a long grassy slope with wild violets on one side, and again, though their stems were short, we gathered all we could find. He knew the one local field where wild orchids grew sparsely, and he took us there to pick. A great prize in the hedgerow was a wild arum, a "lord" or "lady", and he helped to pick every one we saw, though we did not much like the small black flies at the bottoms of the tube.

The value of wild flowers changed with the season. A thin little buttercup, poking up from grass in March, was a wonder. But by May when the fields were golden we did not bother about the million flowers. It was the same with a succession of blooms – clovers and milkmaids and wild roses – which were treasurers at first but then increased and almost lost their charm.

But once we had picked a flower it became our child, not to be

7

abandoned. Other pickers were not as conscientious. At bluebell time cyclists would pass with huge bundles of flowers, more than anybody could want, drooping from their handlebars. Often we found scattered flowers thrown down at the edge of the road. We would long to take them home to revive them, but this was not allowed. Flowers picked by unknown people were "dirty". All we could do was to arrange them in a puddle or a damp ditch and hope that they would enjoy their wet beds. George would wait impatiently or stroll on.

At last, footsore, we would limp home, each with a wilting bunch of mixed trophies. We would plump down on the old ottoman and unlace and kick off our shoes, and feel we could never move again. But the flowers were our children – temporarily – and soon we would stagger up to thrust our drooping handfuls into vases, running the water on them with almost a physical sense of relief. The flowers smelt of Eden, and we would arrange the vases along our morning-room mantelpiece, and only then take off our coats and groan and quarrel about who was to get the tea. The flowers would gently scent the room for a few days, but then the water would turn green and the stalks slimy and the petals would fall and the bunch become a clotted mass, children no more. And they would be thrown into the dustbin with ashes and old meat-bones.

Rosetta was the one adult of whom we were never afraid. Small and stooping with grey blouses and long black skirts, with a wad of pink thermogene wool on her chest in winter, she was always fluttery and gentle. One could not be afraid of her, but she sometimes embarrassed us by asking, "Do you love Jesus, darling?". We would mutter "Yes" and then wonder if we had told a lie.

Rosetta, like the rest of her family, loved cats as well as the Lord, though George did not. He submitted to her fancies, however, and on Christmas afternoon, the only time in the year when Rosetta came out to tea, he would break his visit by a return to "Vellmead" to see that it was not burgled and give the cats their evening meal.

Rosetta, who had become a recluse, was master in some things, but it was probably George who in the past had imposed a strict religious routine on the family. The Sabbath to them was Sunday, and it must be a day of rest except for church-going. The week-end joint and fruit pie were cooked on Saturday and eaten cold on Sunday. The girls might not read novels or knit or do needlework on the day of rest, and to the end of her life the eldest daughter, Lucy, could not bring herself to do needlework or knit on Sunday, though she had to clothe four children. "I don't *feel* it's right," she would say.

As they grew older the girls hated Sunday, and yet the family religion brought them an elevated happiness. After attending the three-hour Good Friday service they greeted Easter Sunday with a rush of joy which they remembered all their lives. Christmas, with its darkness, decorations and carols, brought a similar happiness.

Rosetta, in the early days of the century, was past adolescent uplift, but her intense religion was part of her eccentricity. She went out only to church and was afraid of many things, including thunder and snakes. She cannot have seen many snakes in Surbiton, and I think now the fear must have come from the tales of missionaries with whom her churches were in contact. She said each winter that she was going to die, and this became almost a family joke. She was too nervous to go to the shops, and her eldest daughter had to look after her in many ways, including ordering her clothes. Rosetta to the end of her life wore costumes of thirty years before, including a black bonnet of gauze on a wire frame and decorated with sequins, tied with strings under the chin. This had to be made for her specially.

But she gave the children one intense pleasure – that of chocolate biscuits. There were sometimes family teas at "Vellmead", and the children were summoned in the morning to choose the delicious squares and rounds which they did not get at home as the biscuits were considered too expensive. "Get plenty," Rosetta would say, giving us about "one-and-six", and in the shop we would watch the dark rings and squares decorated with crystallised roses and violets being slipped into a paper bag and feel like queens.

Rosetta's teas were lavish, with slices of squashy very white new bread and very yellow butter and a pot of very red strawberry jam. Little glass gold-topped jars held meat or fish paste, and there was always one of Rosetta's rich fruit cakes said to be so good because it was baked so slowly in the range. It was too early in the century for salad stuff to be included, but we did not like lettuce anyhow.

Rosetta was accused by the family of being obstinate in her narrow world, and she did not quite follow George in religious worship.

9

He was "low church" and a pillar of the local St. Matthew's, but she took a fancy to St. Mark's, another large Victorian neo-Gothic church up the hill nearly a mile away. So she accompanied George to his church on Sunday evenings, but if weather permitted she attended St. Mark's in the morning, recruiting a grandchild to walk her up the hill.

She went at a snail's pace; so one had to be at "Vellmead" an hour before the service. We crept out, Rosetta in her black bonnet and long-waisted black satin coat. She was afraid of the mild traffic of Sunday morning, and would draw back several times before crossing the road. Sometimes she would give a little start when we met people. But we arrived at last in the leafy, churchyard, and entered the church a quarter of an hour early, when it was nearly empty. Rosetta was a little deaf and did not trouble what the world thought of her. She crept with a bashful grandchild up the aisle to the very front pew.

In her frailty she took her own way with the service, sitting in the long parts when the rest of the congregation stood. The grandchild, afflicted with the adolescent habit of feeling faint, was quite glad to be spared from standing in the long psalms, but they both stood for the shorter more dashing hymns. Occasionally the florid kindly vicar, whom they both adored, gave them a little smile as he swished by in his white surplice.

We emerged feeling at peace with heaven, and crept tranquilly back down the hill. But summer does not last, and soon we were in the season of cold, smoking fires and bronchitis. Rosetta always developed bronchitis in winter and always announced that she was dying. She was proved wrong many times, but when she reached seventy-three, a good age in those days, she was right.

In the dark December days she lay against a rampart of pillows in the big white bed among the portraits of clergy. At first it seemed that the bronchitis would clear up as it had before, but this time it turned to pneumonia. Rosetta had to have somebody with her all the time, and on a Saturday morning my mother asked me, then aged sixteen, to take charge briefly while she went shopping.

Rosetta looked odd to me with her thin grey-brown hair in a small plait. At first she was quiet, but then she began to babble. She became distressed and cried that a horse with a trap had bolted and was running down the road outside, and everybody would be killed.

I insisted there was no horse, but it was a mistake. Suddenly she leapt out of bed and flung herself on the sofa by the window. I tried to draw her back, but she shook me off, gazing frantically out at the road. "Look," she cried. "They'll all be upset and killed".

It was no good arguing. A little proud of my strategy I said, "It's all right now. They've gone round the corner." And to my surprise she quietened. "So they have," she said, and allowed herself to be led back to bed.

She was quiet for a few minutes and then began to babble again. This time she cried that the Pope was hovering overhead and was going to take her away. I had never heard my grandparents mention the Pope before, but her period had been full of bitter feuds between Church of Rome and Church of England, and he must have become a bogeyman to her.

Again I argued, but again it was no good. The Pope was up there and he had come for her. She sprang up in bed, and I tried to hold her down, yielding to a resort to force. But she was extraordinarily strong and fought me, calling me a wicked girl. I grew agitated too and tried to hold her hands, afraid all the time that I was doing her harm. In the midst of the struggle my mother walked in.

I felt that I had committed a fearful crime – fighting with the holy Rosetta. But somehow my mother quietened her and even apologised to me. She had not meant to be so long away. "I met somebody. You go and have your dinner now," she said quite kindly. I was a child again, sheltered from responsibility. Relieved, I crept away.

But that was not quite the end. A little before her death Rosetta became lucid again and said to my mother that she was afraid that she had been "unkind to Gwenny." She said that she was very sorry.

I was freed from guilt. But it was a lesson to be learned many times this century – that intense beliefs do not always bring peace and happiness. Rosetta herself with her "nerves" did not perhaps have a very cheerful life, but she had some comforts beside Jesus – her cats and her grandchildren.

# CHAPTER 3

# Shakespeare and House-Hunting

Shakespeare is the king of the century, a national symbol – at least, if not Shakespeare himself a pretend Shakespeare. Of course the public reads poetry no more and ignores everything written before our century unless television has recommended it. And in performances, as with concerts, it is the producers and performers who head the announcement of the event, and the music or play comes second. It is the producers, not the author, who are discussed in Shakespeare programmes. And there is an air of apology that the plays are not "with it", and they must be modernised – set in India, or with crinolines, or with jeans, or acted by puppets. The Elizabethan writer has almost disappeared under a load of twentieth-century business. However, if you ask almost any adult who Shakespeare was he will probably know.

Bit I did not expect Shakespeare's appearance in my house-hunting after the war.

I had been working in Birmingham, but after the war had a new job in a London office. I needed a house and naturally turned back to the Redbury area where I had spent my childhood. But I soon found that house-hunting was a monstrous task.

House-building had ceased during the war and thousands of dwellings had been lost through bombing. In Redbury small houses with two and a half bedrooms were being occupied by two generations of six or seven people. I was told dark stories of Government agencies sneaking round looking for houses that could be commandeered for offices. People who had sold their houses and were waiting for a new occupier left the curtains up and a piano in the window so that the house should not appear empty and be threatened.

I was working in the week and could house-hunt only at the weekends. Advertisements and agents did their best to glorify what property they had to sell. I was sent to a "spacious family house" to find a decayed privet hedge, a shabby Edwardian door and a smell of damp and mice. A "personally designed house" turned out to have a downstairs room with an alcove which had been an office and a bathroom downstairs and nowhere much to sit. I met an agreeable policeman who was being transferred and motored me out to a small suitable house with the right price; but it was in the country with little contact with a station.

A friend in one of Redbury's older polite roads sent me to a house opposite. "I know that the people are moving. You can only ask." Doubtfully I went across to the wide front gate to find a lady with plucked eyebrows and a small gentleman bending over flower beds. The lady came to the gate, heard my faltering enquiry, and said, "We're moving to Ireland because of the dreadful taxation here. But you would not be able to pay for this house anyhow. We want four thousand pounds." Four thousand pounds for a house! Incredible! I had only two thousand to spend, and the mortgage boom was only in its infancy. I retreated humiliated.

After months of search I was sent to a small house with a suitable situation and price. I told the owner that I would return with friends after lunch to confirm the sale. But when I came back in two hours the house has been sold to another group who had not hesitated. I felt near despair.

Then in my weekly call to an agent he suggested that I should look at a house a mile up the long main road. I walked up but did not go in. It was a small terrace house and bound to be noisy, I thought, with the main road so near. And the front garden was choked with bricks and planks, and the owner was asking too high a price. The only thing I liked was a line of young poplars along the front and down one side. The twigs were inter-weaving and were a soft pink in the December morning half-sun. But I said to the agent, "Too noisy and too expensive."

But by the end of another fortnight nothing suitable had come on the market. The agent said, "Why don't you go and look at that house again? The owner has bought another house and is in a hurry to move, and he's dropped his price." So for a second time I walked up the long road. The poplars were really very pretty, and there was a stout privet hedge down the side, so that the front garden, in spite of the bricks, had a secluded air. And the path sloped down a little so that the porch was below the level of the road, and this, I thought, might lessen the traffic noise.

So I went down the path and rang, and a small sandy-haired man opened the door. And so I met the descendant of William Shakespeare.

The smell of Sunday dinner being cooked came out in a warm breath. It was homely and reassuring. I stepped inside, and Bert Hall said that he had a young son and a teen-age daughter, and his parents were staying in the house as well. That meant six people, and I thought that, if they could all squeeze in, the place must be large enough for me.

Mr Hall was very amiable and took me round. The warm house seemed a refuge after the chill outside. We went up the narrow stairs, and peered into the half-room where the boy slept with Mickey Mouse scraps on the wall. As a contrast the down-stairs front room had two elegant versions of Shakespeare. In the centre of the mantelpiece was a highly glazed pottery bust with a creamy face, bright red lips, a well-trimmed pointed beard and the obligatory domed brow. In an upper pane of the window appeared a coloured glass roundel with another exquisite Bard, this time in profile with another domed brow and dandified beard.

Mr Hall waved at the window "If you take the house you must let me remove the Shakespeares."

"Certainly," I said, "and the Mickey Mouses upstairs."

"You see," Mr Hall said, presumably alluding to the Bard," he was my ancestor."

"Impossible," I said tactlessly. "Shakespeare's family died out."

But "No. Not at all," Bert Hall assured me. Shakespeare's daughter had married a Hall, hadn't she? And the family had gone on – he didn't quite know how – to his grandfather and them to him. He was definitely a great-great – a lot of greats – descendant of the Bard.

I did not argue. There were too many other things to discuss. I stayed for half an hour while Mr Hall expatiated on the good materials and convenience of the house. Was it not noisy?, I asked. No, he said. They never heard the traffic. This was not my subsequent experience, and the road became busier through the years; but one grows used to these things.

14

I asked him why he wanted to leave such a paragon of a dwelling, and he replied very reasonably that his family needed more space. He had bought a larger house nearer to London and wanted to move as soon as possible. Of course his esteemed ancestor had bought a substantial property, though that was out of London.

I was weary of house-hunting, and this small place had a lived-in feeling. Through hesitation I had lost one possible home, and I was afraid of losing another. I told Bert Hall that I would let him know in an hour. I walked away down the road and when I reached a telephone box rang up and said I would take his offer.

In the next few weeks I found Mr Hall very obliging. He mentioned his great ancestor several times and removed the bust from the mantelpiece and the roundel from the window. The Mickey Mouses went too and a huge litter of builder's rubbish from the gardens. It was a great improvement, though chunks of concrete were left behind.

In the long narrow back garden Mr Hall dwelt on its beauties, though these could not be checked as it was December. A row of young poplars was here too with a stout privet hedge on the other side, but, as with other plants, it seemed that his knowledge did not quite equal his great ancestor's. He talked of primroses, violets and roses and three young apple trees. I never saw primroses or violets, and, though there were some pale rambler roses under the poplars, they soon died out in the shade. The three small fruit trees bore not apples but coarse plums which did provide jam, but they had been planted across the middle of the garden, which would have been cut in two if they had been allowed to grow there. We had them moved to the end, but one blew over. However, the other two sheltered us a little from the ranks of small houses at the back.

The small lawn, thin because of the poplars, had a dilapidated little wooden bird table in the centre, but what the garden was really rich in was concrete. The path, like all other paths about us, were of concrete and, we found, harboured many ants in their cracks. Concrete boulders were spread lavishly over a sloping bed, and it seemed that Bert Hall had been trying, unsuccessfully, to make a rock garden; but weeds had prevailed. I was reminded of the speech on weeds in *Henry V.* I struggled with the boulders for years, but at last a friend bashed them up, and we put the small pieces, bit by bit, into the dustbin. But still odd chunks turn up.

Before Mr Hall moved out he asked me earnestly if I had antiques to sell. A high shelf ran round the sitting-room of his new house, and he wanted to arrange articles worthy of his ancestor along it. I had just inherited some Victorian silver and other trifles which I had hardly examined, but I did not want to bother with them and was too busy to have them valued. I wanted to oblige Mr Hall, and I said he could have them for ten pounds, though heaven knew what they were really worth. I pointed out that they were not of Shakespeare's period. That did not matter, Bert Hall said, as long as they were *old*. He seemed pleased, though he did not pay at once. He said he would send a cheque.

We moved in and found some disadvantages in the ideal dwelling, but that was inevitable. The money for the silver did not come; so I wrote and reminded Bert Hall of his debt. Ten pounds was a substantial sum in the later 1940s. No answer came; so I wrote again. This time two pounds arrived with a scrawl on a smudged bit of paper. Bert Hall said I owed the rest for some painting he had done. This had been part of the original agreement and had not been mentioned before. But he was probably hard up and I was busy, and it seemed useless to continue the argument. After all, the Bard had the reputation of being an argumentative businessman.

Mr Hall vanished and was speedily forgotten as happens in our shifting community. Somebody told me later that he had moved again but where was not known. It might have been to Stratford-upon-Avon, but I do not think so. He was a London type with a flat Surrey accent, and no doubt felt the attraction of the capital as Shakespeare himself did.

For some months our neighbours on the south side did not speak to us. When at last conversation did begin they excused themselves by saying that they had thought we were "friends of Hall's". They had been quarrelling with him for a long time. Hence the poplars to shut them out.

They told me that before the war Bert Hall had been an ordinary builder's assistant. But, presumably with work for the Forces, he had made money and set up for himself. It was then that the legend of

Shakespeare ancestry began, and he went about boasting of his famous forbear. He was an unlettered man, and how he had found out about Shakespeare's daughter they did not know.

They were naturally critical of him, and they added that he was a mean man who was always sending his children round to borrow something – even a jug of hot water in summer when they did not want to light gas. In the end after years of borrowing they had rebelled and there had been a quarrel.

While the Bard left behind immortal works, Bert left concrete and poplars. We cursed the concrete for years, and the poplars were pretty but quite unsuitable for a small garden, and they had to be felled in the end.

Shakespeare ascribed "self and vain deceit" to kings. He might have added small builders.

# CHAPTER 4
## Children and a Devil

Children and their upbringing have been among the chief arguments of the century. The early 1900s inherited the Bible and strict moral rulings, but Freud and the study of psychology formed a counter-blast. Were children descended "from God who is our home", as Wordsworth thought, or were they vessels of original sin? Were they shaped by heredity or environment? Should we let them develop as they liked and only try to make them happy? Or should we discipline and punish them to fit them for society?

The questions continue, unresolved. Meanwhile good and bad children appear, the worst probably little boys and adolescent girls. But we cannot even be sure if they are bad or good, as they change so rapidly. They are secretive too, and you never really know what is in their minds.

So you may get surprises as we did with our devil David.

At the bottom of our gardens a concreted alleyway ran parallel with the main road. Another line of back gardens was on the other side, so that it was a retired place with almost no traffic. Here, when my two boys were young, the children of the houses round us used to gather to play games and sometimes fight.

The alley was convenient for busy mothers except that they could not see it from their kitchens. They could only listen and go down now and then. Sometimes there was screaming, and a child came up to complain. At other times two or three would come up for biscuits. As I worked in the week I was anxious to be agreeable at week-ends. Other neighbours guarded their property against the children; so our garden became a kind of annexe to the alley.

Among the children was David, eight years old, sandy-haired and pre-eminent for wickedness. He came from a small house holding grandparents, parents and a new baby that occupied his mother, and at week-ends the door was locked on him and he was told to go and play. He had an agreeable manner, and his favourite phrase was "I never" which stood for "I never done it." But he always had.

He banged dustbin lids till he nearly drove the neighbours mad. He delighted and horrified the children by urinating against a lamppost. His informal language was full of "buggers". He came up to ask for biscuits, knocked a bowl down and broke it and ran away. He broke the children's toys, leaving fragments on the grass. Once with his soft voice he offered to help me trim the hedge. Before I could stop him he had seized the children's shears and gone round demolishing the bluebells.

Stories circulated about his sins. At the other side of the alley lived an elderly Irish woman who loved children and had none of her own. She used to stand at her back gate and hand out sweets and biscuits. She told me one day that she had gone out one afternoon leaving three pots of hyacinths by her back door to get an airing. David walked up her garden and broke them all. She added resignedly, "I don't suppose he means any harm. Everything he touches breaks."

At last I rebelled. "Don't let David in any more," I told my boys, but it was not easy to get rid of him. A garage and trees were at the end of our garden, and it was simple for David to creep in and hide. So a campaign developed. I would go down the garden when I thought he was there, and he would run out. But directly I turned my back he would creep in again. In the end I grew tired of chasing him. My boys, who secretly admired him, said they could not keep him out.

At Christmas my boys were given a yoyo, a fashionable toy of the moment. They took it into the garden on Christmas morning and came in to dinner without it. They had not learned to work it and I had hardly seen it.

"David's got it," they said.

After dinner David did not come into the garden as usual; so I went down to the alley. He was just outside our gate, trying to pull a sliver of loose wood from the garage.

"Don't do that David. And where is our yoyo?"

"Took it home to my mum," he said carelessly.

"Well where is it?"

"She's broke it," he said tranquilly. "No good now."

19

Could I go round and knock on David's mother's door and complain that she had broken our yoyo? I had not the courage. We never saw the yoyo again.

A terrifying incident with David occurred one early November. We were having a bonfire at the bottom of the garden on a mild afternoon a few days after Bonfire Night. At that time when most young families had their own fireworks, and bonfires were in most small gardens, children in Redbury went round the alleys afterwards looking for the decorative coloured papers and other remnants. But these had now been gathered, and ours was only a useful bonfire to burn garden rubbish.

I had sent David away, as he had tried to stamp on the glowing ashes with thin plimsoles. But he had crept back unnoticed while I was attending to the fire. It crackled cheerfully, and the children held out their hands to the blaze.

Suddenly there was a colossal, terrifying bang. The fire blew out in all directions scattering us with dust. I thought that I was deafened for life. Slowly intelligence returned, and I was aware of a stupefied silence and then a chorus of voices from other gardens: "What was that? What is it?". Then I noticed a faint simper on David's face. He saw me looking and began the usual, "I never ..."

But as usual he had. One of the girls had seen him. He must have picked up a live firework in the alley. Of course he had known that it was live but possibly not how powerful it was. I thought afterwards that somebody might have been killed. Once more he was sent away.

But in a few days he was back for more mischief. On one occasion he was in the garden with a girl friend. She was helping to cut the hedge and giving him turns with the small shears. I was just telling him that he was being useful for once when there was a thundering at our back gate, tall and solid. "He's locked it," the girl murmured.

Shouting rose outside. "David. Are yer there, yer young devil?"

We stopped working. "But she can't get in," the girl whispered, looking frightened. We stood and held our breaths. But the grandmother knew that David was there. "Come out, or I'll..." and she thumped till I thought the gate would collapse.

But of course one cannot keep a boy if his grannie is after him. "Go along David," I said.

20

He knew that doom was ahead. He slunk with a hangdog look and unlocked the gate. It was thrust open, and David was dragged outside. There was a howl and a shout of "I'll teach yer, yer young devil." The grannie spoke more softly as she realised that people were listening. "I'll give you such a hiding." Then the threats and howls retreated down the alley.

The other children looked quite shaken, but we never discovered what David had done.

Skirmishes were frequent in the alley. At one moment the children would be playing quietly; at the next two boys would be wrestling. If some loud noise continued I went down to see what was wrong. If the children wanted anything – generally food – they came up to me in the kitchen.

One morning David appeared bleeding. He said that my younger boy had thrown a stone and hit him. I did not enquire into the incident. All the children told tales of one another, and I did not encourage their complaints. But now David's head was wounded. "You'd better go home," I said. But no, no. He could not go home till dinner-time. So I mopped his hair till the bleeding stopped and cleaned him up though a mark remained on his rather grimy collar. He said in his soft way, "Thank you. I'm all right now."

Once more I urged him to go home, but he had been turned out and must stay out. Later I heard him shouting in the alley, and I almost forgot the incident. But that afternoon, just as we were going out, there came a long peal at the front door. It sounded an announcement of disaster. I hurried to answer, and there stood David's pretty mother glaring. "I want to know why your boy hit our David." Her voice rose. "Nearly killed him he did."

Surprise made me dumb. Anyhow there was no chance to speak in the flood of fury. "Cut his head open, and then you leave him to bleed. Comes home with blood all over him. Assault it is. If the child had bled to death it would have been your fault."

She shouted on. In the fifties, Redbury people were not as genteel as today, and they listened to neighbours' quarrels. No doubt there were greedy ears now. The only way to stop her was to shut the door.

I began to edge it to. "You're not fit to look after children," she shouted. I said "Goodbye" and got the door shut. There was a blessed silence. Then the gate was banged violently.

Once more I told the boys to keep away from David, but without much hope of being obeyed.

A week later there was another urgent ring at our front door. My heart sank, but one had to answer it of course. There stood David's mother again and, behind her, his rather ill-shaved father.

But now David's mother smiled sweetly. She said politely, "We're collecting for old Mrs Cole. The funeral's on Tuesday, and the neighbours are sending a few flowers. If you could spare a copper or two..."

I was so much relieved that I would have given her a fortune. As it was I offered half-a-crown.

"Very good of you," David's mother said sweetly, and the two tripped away and did not bang the gate.

I wondered afterwards if she had a short memory or if it was an apology.

The boys themselves went on playing together. One Saturday morning I found my elder boy and David at the bottom of the garden contemplating a pile of wood strips. The boys were looking it over as if wondering what to do with it.

"What's all this?" I asked fearful of more mischief.

But there was no mischief this time. "Me Dad gave it to us to play with," David said. David's family making some contribution to the general entertainment! I could hardly believe it. I said it was awfully good of David's dad to give them the wood, and David might stay a little.

But the next day our odd-job man, who had come to do some small tasks and was taller than I was, looked over the top of the garage. " 'Ere. 'Ere," he said. "Who's been stripping the roof? You've got a big bare patch. *And* they've been chucking the bits all over the place."

"Oh no," I said. "That wood's been sent by a neighbour."

Our odd-job man looked more closely. "It wasn't, you know." He picked up one of the strips. "Look. It fits, doesn't it? And that bit's come from there. The roof's been wrecked."

My boy stared down shame-faced. He hardly ever told lies, but now he was caught. He confessed later that he had been with David on the roof – a thing I had forbidden – but David had done all the stripping. It was David who had made up the story of his father's gift.

The repairs were followed by a large bill. "Tell David I want to see him," I said to my boys. But David did not come near our garden, and there was no sign of him when I went into the alley. Only once I saw him at a distance with his girl friend, and then he turned to flee. But I called after him, "Why did you wreck our garage?"

He had to stop, but he said in his old soft way, "I never... No, I never..."

"No, he didn't ever..." corroborated his girl friend.

I came up with them. "It wasn't me done it," David assured me.

Of course he would have told the same story to his parents. I looked up and saw his father digging in his garden. I had seen David's embattled mother, and I had not the courage to walk in and complain. I said only, "You're a naughty little boy," and walked away.

For a few weeks David continued to avoid me; so we had some peace. Then the boys brought in a rumour that David's family were going to move. They had found a house on the other side of the road.

Our road had become like a railway, almost completely dividing the two sides by its stream of traffic. The news of the move greatly cheered the neighbours who also had suffered from David, and it was the best thing that had happened to me for a long time.

David came back once or twice to play in the alley. Then he disappeared and, like smaller irritants that cease to trouble, he was forgotten.

It must have been about two years later when we met again.

We had boarded a bus on a Sunday afternoon, and David's family got in at the next stop. Parents and children were decked out for Sunday. David's mother was still young and pretty and was elegant in summer blue, and David's father was more closely shaved than usual. The toddler was in yellow, and David, taller and more angular, with his hair sleeked down, wore a navy blazer. With his young brother he sat down demurely in front of us.

David's mother smiled affably. David, with his old innocent look, turned to say good afternoon. He was now a perfect little gentleman. "Say afternoon to the lady," he told the toddler.

"A-noon," the obedient toddler said.

"There's a good Johnny," David said, and gave him a smacking kiss on the top of his head. Then he began a dissertation on the traffic.

"There's an Austin. Look," he said kindly. "There's an ambulance. Look at that man on a motor-bike. Look at that garridge and the cars getting petrol."

Family affection, cleanliness, courtesy – all the virtues – emanated from the dark blue blazer. David sat, his arm round his brother's shoulders, and peace spread through the bus.

Many years later I heard that David had married and had a good job with an electrical firm.

# CHAPTER 5

# Pets and the Cat that Died Twice

One of the greatest changes in our century has been in our attitude towards pets. There have always been lovers of individual animals – Alexander with his horse, Dr Johnson and Edward Lear with their cats, Elizabeth Browning with her dog – but generally animals have had no rights. Kind adults last century urged children not to pull Pussy's tail and boys not to tie tin cans to cats' tails. But ill treatment was common – dogs tied up for life and pets killed in barbarous ways. The Cats Protection League was formed only in 1927 when crowds of outcast cats were roaming city streets.

At the beginning of the century there were almost no vets to look after pets. Today a host of vets make good livings. Pet-food production is an enormous business, and we have pets' comforts of many kinds. Pet laws, charities, societies, journals, Christmas cards and television programmes accompany our days. Animal enthusiasts set fire to laboratories, confront huntsmen and risk their lives to protect whales. Our attitude to the animal world has become a moral – though puzzling – issue.

Our Gin lived just after the war when the change was taking place. He was born in a coal cupboard in back-quarter London, but moved to greater comfort at Redbury. But the change during his short life was not complete. He died through swarming modern traffic, but also through an old-fashioned not very competent vet.

I met Mrs Smith through a London settlement. She lived near Waterloo Station on the first floor of a decrepit building by a railway arch, and she wanted visits. She was in her seventies with sharp black eyes and wispy greying hair, and I visited her on Thursday evenings after work.

To reach her I went up a grimy staircase to a landing with a dirty sink and dripping tap. It was just after the war, and property was in a bad state. Her room had a rusty gas-stove, sagging chairs, a bed behind a tattered curtain and a rickety table by the window with a dusty aspidistra. In a coal cupboard lived two cats.

Mrs Smith smoked as many cigarettes as she could afford, and sometimes sent me out to buy her some more fags. The smoke may have discouraged the flies on warm summer evenings, but it cannot have been good for the cats – a pretty little tortoiseshell named Dolly and her orange kitten Woggles. Dolly had regular batches of kittens, and Mrs Smith drowned them all. But the orange kitten was particularly pretty; so she saved him and said I should have him when I got a house.

I sat on a sagging chair, and Mrs Smith gave me magenta fancy cakes and strong tea. She had been married to a barman, and she told me stories of her lively past. The cats would emerge and scutter about, and Mrs Smith would control them with a bamboo cane, whacking out at them and making them cower. "I take it to bed with me at night," she told me, "and when they make too much noise I whack the floor. That shuts them up."

She had taught Woggles a pretty trick, putting a piece of cake between her lips and holding it out, when the kitten would sidle up and snatch it. She told me that Woggles was "a very clean cat, and always goes outside for his business." He would jump on to the wobbly table by the window, climb through the window, scramble along a sill and down a pipe and skirt the building to a patch behind. This led to a feud with the old lady living below, for she fed sparrows and Woggles went after them. She would emerge at the bottom of the stairs as I came in and mutter about "them damned dratted animals." She did not get on well with Mrs Smith, who answered her back.

For months Mrs Smith cleared up her room for me and gave me tea. Then I got my house and took Woggles. Soon afterwards Mrs Smith had a fall and was moved to a local old-fashioned hospital. I visited her once, and found her very clean but listless in an interminably long ward with blank old faces along the sides. She reacted in the normal way by dying in a few weeks. It turned out that she had a daughter, who came and cleared the room and had the faithful Dolly destroyed.

But by that time Woggles was far away. I shall never forget the journey with him on that winter evening. Mrs Smith supplied an old wicker hamper, and had thrown in a bit of raw fish to make it attractive. I did not realise this for a week, as I left the hamper in our garden, but when I took it back to my office to return it at my next visit to Mrs Smith I noticed a curious smell and investigated. Woggles had not touched the fish, and it went down the office lavatory.

But on the evening of the cat's exit we pushed him protesting, now fully grown, into the hamper. As I carried it to Waterloo Station he shifted his weight from side to side and moaned continually. Now and then a furry arm would curl out of holes in the wickerwork.

He was still moaning as I lugged him up the steps at Waterloo Station and on to the platform, but in the corridor of the train his moans ceased. Either he liked the motion or he was dumb with fear. I swayed him in silence over the steps of the home station, but in the bus queue he began to moan again, and people started and looked round. The bus conductor greeted me with, "Come on Dick," and then, as I didn't understand, added "Whittington."

Thankfully I heaved the hamper down to the pavement at the home bus-stop; hurried across the road, and with enormous relief opened the front door and lifted the hamper lid. A frantic form shot out and disappeared upstairs. Perhaps he thought he would find his old coal cupboard again. When he did not find it he crept under a bed. It was cold up there in the days before we had central heating, but we could not coax him down. We pushed saucers of milk and fish under the bed, but he did not touch them, and if we tried to get hold of him he retreated into a dark corner.

For more than a day Woggles stayed in the chilly dusk. I went to work, but we was still there when I returned. On the second morning my housekeeper decided that he must "do his business" as Mrs Smith said, and she managed to get hold of him and carry him downstairs into the garden. Light snow was on the ground, but she put him down and stayed beside him. She told me that he did not move or make any effort to relieve himself, and they stood together for some minutes. Then she gave up and carried him back, marvelling at cats' control of their functions.

Woggles streaked upstairs again, and stayed under the bed for another day.

But in the end he settled down. We got him to a fire, and he lapped some milk. Then he began to eat and learnt where we kept

27

his saucer, leading us into the kitchen and gazing hopefully up at us. Then he tripped down the back steps and sheltered under the hedge, and then went under it and strayed through other gardens, his orange fur and white front looking pretty in the spring green. Then, as warm nights arrived, he began his orgies.

I knew little about cats in those days and imagined that, as Woggles had not been neutered in early youth, the time for it had passed. There was no vet near and we were over-busy caring for my adopted baby; so Woggles's ecstasies continued spring after spring. Sometimes he disappeared for a day or two, but generally his females came to him. In the evening our garden would be full of howls and moans, gleaming eyes and scuttering feet. In a way I was glad. The cat had had a hard beginning, and now he was enjoying one of nature's pleasures. At least I supposed it was enjoyment, although it turned him into a scarecrow. His coat dimmed, and stiff points of fur stood out round his neck where his sweethearts had chewed it. Our neighbour said, "Your cat looked like a skeleton. I didn't think he'd get through the summer."

He was, of course, a nuisance to the neighbours who had female cats. His offspring began to appear in gardens round. At one time I counted five, almost exactly like him but a little paler. He never showed any interest in these young cats which, being orange, were presumably male by the cats' colour code.

Meanwhile we had the smells. Woggles was always particularly affectionate when he smelt worst. He would rub round our legs, and we would move away. Then he would leap on to his favourite chair, and we would shift him and put paper on it. Cat smells would be round table legs and corners, and we would go round with a cloth and bleach.

By this time he has ceased to be Woggles. My housekeeper called him Ginny because of his ginger colour. The neighbours thought he was Jenny and a female, but the new name seemed more fitting for a young graceful cat.

However, though his name was changed, he was still influenced by his past. He never played with a ball or string, and if we dangled string before his nose he only sniffed it and turned away. The bamboo cane seemed still a memory. So was the old diet of cake. After I had put out tea for visitors he would slip in, and I would find half-eaten tarts dragged across the cloth, the edge of a sponge nibbled and butter licked from scones. Soon I learned to keep the door shut when tea was put out.

We fed him mainly on "pussies' pieces" from the fishmonger, since tins of cat food had not come in. He was also fond of egg. His early experience and the cane had made him face the world with suspicion and he was fond of us but unfriendly to strangers. He would lash out if he were touched and then run into a corner, and if he met inoffensive dogs he would hump his back and spit. He had one close cat friend for a time, but that was a sad story.

The friend came from one of the small houses at the back – we never quite knew from which. He had longish hair and was portly with short legs so that when he walked his abdomen almost touched the ground. We called him Black Slug.

In spite of his fat he loved climbing. He would scramble on to the roof of our small porch, claw up the slope to a bedroom window, thrust through an open casement and flop on to the bed below. He would bump to the ground, patter down the stairs and stop by the front door, asking to be let out to do the climb again. Gin would watch him but not follow.

Most people who keep cats acknowledge some paranormal senses in them. Gin was to show these very clearly. Certainly he had some mental link with Black Slug which annoyed us. We used to put Gin's food out in the yard in summer and he would lope down the kitchen steps to it. But he would not eat it but stand by the saucer with his head slightly raised and stare down the garden. After a minute or two Black Slug would appear at the end and amble up the path. The two would then eat amicably together. This meant that much or our cat food went to the visitor who certainly did not look as if he needed it.

But Black Slug became a familiar figure, and we were shocked when the friendship came to an end. He ceased to appear, and a neighbour remarked casually that his family had grown tired of him and had him "bumped off". Such blithe murder would be less likely today.

Gin, however, continued to show his paranormal gifts. This was mainly when we went away on holidays and left him to the care of housekeeper or neighbour. Once or twice he disappeared for some days but was back to greet us when we returned. Once we found him

29

waiting under the front hedge and once he got in through a window and was waiting in his favourite armchair. "Well I'm jiggered," our help said. "I haven't seen him for days."

His most sensational feat was one January when we went away for a week. I thought he would be cold at home; so my housekeeper said that she would look after him in her maisonette. This was almost a mile away with alternative travel, involving main roads, a bus route up a hill, a meeting of ways and a descent to a small estate by fields. But my housekeeper was fond of animals and he knew her well; so we did not expect any problems.

I carried Gin in a closed basket, from which he could have seen nothing. We went by bus. He had moaned a little on the journey, perhaps remembering the travel from London. I took him up the stairs to our help's maisonette, and when the door was shut opened the basket. Gin did exactly as he had done before – went under furniture, this time a cupboard, and refused to come out. Yet he knew my help and she had a bright fire and a saucer of food for him. She was piqued at his surliness but prided herself on her way with animals. "He'll settle down all right."

When we got home a week later Gin was sitting calmly on our shed roof. It was a cold afternoon, but he did not seem to mind, following us into the house and asking for a meal. We assumed that our help had brought him home early, but when she arrived she shook her fist at him. "That dratted cat. First he wouldn't move from under the cupboard, though I put down some nice fish. In the morning I thought I must take him out to do his business. It was a foggy morning; so I didn't take him far – just to the green behind the house. I watched beside him, but he didn't do anything and I got cold, I went in for two minutes. When I came out again he'd disappeared."

She said that she had searched for two hours in the fog, but given up at last. Later she had come down to our house to see if there was any post. "And there blow me if the cat wasn't sitting on the shed, as cheeky as you please. I could have murdered him. After that I didn't dare move him, and had to come down to feed him each day."

Gin showed no sign of distress and peacefully continued his old habits, but we wondered how he had travelled. There were several routes that he could have taken, especially as he was no respecter of private gardens. As there was fog he had no sun to steer by – if cats do steer by the sun. He had had to negotiate traffic, but he could not have taken long over the journey as our help had found him in the afternoon of the day when he had disappeared. He had not been previously more than a few gardens away from our home, and he had seen absolutely nothing on the journey out.

We were only thankful that he had not tried to walk back to London.

It was not long afterwards that we were visited by tragedy. On a relaxed Sunday morning Paul, not yet four, and I were sitting at breakfast. We had given Gin some of our egg, and he had asked to go out at the front door, leapt over a fence and disappeared. Almost immediately a knock came on the door. A stout unknown woman was there. She asked, "Have you got a ginger cat?" I said we had. "Well he's been run over. He's on the other side of the road. Dead, I'm afraid."

Of course, Gin had a habit of darting into the road and trusting to luck to see him through. I walked to the gate. Opposite, stretched on the grass verge, was a small orange body. "I'll stay with the child if you want to go and see," the woman said kindly. I nerved myself and went across.

He lay with his lips drawn back in a snarl – all teeth. He must have run a long way before he dropped, for he was far up on the grass verge. I could not see any damage, but he was certainly dead. He seemed paler than in life. His fur had lost its glowing colour. He looked draggled, a piece of rubbish, and I could feel only a shudder of distaste. I returned and thanked the woman, and she left gravely and quietly as at a human death.

I did not bring the body in. An official scavenger was going the rounds, and he would know what to do with it. It did not matter to Ginny what we did with him now. But the sense of loss grew. I should not have to call at the fishmonger's the next day. I should be able to shut up at night without seeing that the cat was in. I should be able to put out tea without shutting the door. There would be no more soft determined rubbing round my ankles.

"We shall have to get a new cat," I said to distract Paul. We finished breakfast, and I thought in the usual baffled way about death. At least we had given Gin a last treat of egg. "What colour shall our next cat be?", I asked Paul. "Green," he said doubtfully. He was not yet sure of cats' colours.

Slowly and softly the sitting-room door opened, and there stood Gin lazily waving his tail. I almost thought that he was a ghost. Then the morning grew bright. Seldom had I felt such deliverance from sorrow. It had all been a bad dream. I fell on Gin and fondled him. I brought him fish and milk. That morning I could hardly let him out of my sight. He must have been surprised at my continuous displays of affection.

The victim must have been one of his sons, who were almost exactly like him but a little paler. I had put the pallor down to death, and the face had been distorted. Within an hour the small corpse had gone from the verge, and everything was the same – except of course that some other family would be grieving. But I was so much absorbed by our resurrection that I did not even try to find them.

But the immortal Gin was not immortal, and he still had the habit of dashing across the road. There was no way of keeping him in the small gardens with their low hedges and fences, and the road became ever more thronged.

"Oh, look at that cat," a startled woman said to me when I was shopping down the road, and there was Gin leaping between car wheels and bonnets which had hardly room to swerve. He was being missed by inches but tearing on. "I can't think how he got through," the woman said.

But then, one Saturday evening, he did not get through.

It was almost a repetition of the previous accident. But now it was a boy who knocked on the door. "We think it's your cat in our garden. He's been hurt."

Three of us went across with him, and here was another mystery. It was Gin certainly, but he was hidden at the end of a long back garden sloping upward, with the house and front garden between it and the road. How had he got there? The boy and his mother did not know. But it seemed that the cat had been hit on the road, and that somehow he had crawled to the garden to hide.

As at other crises we wished that cats could talk. We called him and he dragged out. He did not seem badly injured; only lame. We carried him back, and he retired to the broom cupboard and was sick.

And then there came one last mystery.

It was Saturday evening in the middle of the century. Animal treatment was improving but had not reached the standards of today. We rang round to all the local vets we could find, and all were either out or would not come. In the end we tried the Police and, with an enormous sense of relief, heard that there was a woman vet, whom the Police themselves used, who had a small van and would come out to accidents. We tried, and, yes, she would come. Blessed relief! She came quite soon; looked Gin over and said that he had only a cracked pelvis. "But I'd like to have him for observation over the week-end," she said. "He can come back to you on Monday."

What could be more reasonable? And the Police had recommended her. It was only some time later, after another of my cats had become infected on her premises, that I heard that they had been declared sub-standard, and she had closed them and gone away. We shall never know now if Gin would have lived if we had kept him at home.

I telephoned on the Sunday, and she said that Gin was doing well and had had a large meal. This was not surprising as he had been sick after the accident. "I'll bring him back tomorrow," the vet said.

But ten minutes later the telephone rang again. "A most unusual thing has happened. Your cat has had a secondary reaction. He has had a seizure. I'm afraid he has died."

It is no good wondering now if we could have saved him, and, as we were to find through the years, cats have very short lives compared with our own, and death and mourning are part of pet-keeping. But Ginny was only eleven years old.

We have had many cats since, but he was our first. I still wish I could feel him, softly and determinedly, rubbing round my legs again.

CHAPTER 6
# Gentry and School Teachers

The word "gentry" has almost gone from our language, and "gentlefolk" themselves have almost disappeared. But when I came across them in the middle of the century they were still in the minds of elderly people. At the beginning of the century the gentry were a social force with their large houses, servants, links with Royalty and penchant for hunting and racing. Now we worship pop stars instead of Tennyson's "Norman blood".

But perhaps the old gentry, with their plumed hats and photographs in the *Bystander*, performed a useful function in boosting our egos. We nearly all want to claim that we are great people in some way, and it was a help to assert that you were an acquaintance of Mrs Smythe-Davenant or Lady Dorset. Much soothing boasting of the kind must have gone on among those longing for respect. We saw it in Hilda Hudd who, though she had only worked for the gentry, plumed herself on the contact. It was she who reminded us of the old "gentry" days.

Hilda in her way was typical of the century. Now that class distinctions have largely gone and the top people of the nation are business magnates or television stars, we can no longer say that an individual is "low class". We say instead that he is "uneducated". Hilda's distinction of knowing gentry developed into that of knowing Miss Rowena Mackey who taught English at the Hellebore High School.

One other form of boasting, which may largely have died out, lingered on in Hilda – the glory of having been born in a certain place. In the old days, before television opened the world out to us, we prided ourselves on being British and not frog-eating French, and, coming closer, honest Yorkshire and not slimy Surrey, and Hilda was very much honest Yorkshire. The North was a nest of hard work, friendliness and warm-heartedness, whereas the South was stuck up, lazy, wealthy and deceitful. Next in honour to Yorkshire came Scotland. Miss Rowena Mackey hailed from Edinburgh. The patriotism of the early century lived on in Hilda, the intense woman whom I met soon after the war.

Hilda was superior from the moment that we met. She was living in a village about three miles away which had once been a beauty spot and had attracted the cultivated and refined. And she occupied a "posh" house – "posh" was a favourite word with her – with Miss Rowena Mackey, who employed her as her housekeeper. Hilda's first remark as she walked through our gate was, "I think this is the smallest house I have ever seen."

I needed a housekeeper to look after the boy that I had adopted, and Hilda had been suggested by a teacher friend who knew Miss Mackey. Hilda was said to be elderly but fond of children. She had been looking after Miss Mackey's doctor father, but he had died and she had not enough to do. She might come to me as a favour. So an interview was fixed for a Saturday afternoon.

It took place well on in the afternoon, for Hilda was very late. I was to find that she was exceedingly vague about time, but that perhaps is a genteel fault. She had the appearance of a haggard and ardent nature-worshipper, with loose wind-blown grey hair, an intense expression and a thick hand-knitted green coatee. She early remarked, as we stood in the back garden, "I ado-ore flowers. Look at that sweet little thing," and she pointed to a sprig of forget-me-not that had poked through a crack in the concrete path. Her drawl indicated her refinement, and, in spite of being a daughter of Yorkshire, she had only a trace of a Northern accent – a sign that she had been connected with the upper classes.

In our first conversation which she dominated I heard something of the gentry and much of Miss Mackey and her adorable doctor father. Hilda also insisted that we must call her "Hilda", as she had been Hilda and not Miss Hudd to the "little people" she had cared for in the past. To give her a surname would have been, we gathered, like giving a surname to a saint. She talked almost without a break for an hour, and said she would come to us but would like every other week-end with Miss Mackey. Then she suddenly realised that it was much later than she had thought and left abruptly. I was exhausted.

But she had seemed attracted to my boy, and I did not want to offend my teacher friend or Miss Mackey. Also I had no-one else in view and, as all working mothers know, it is impossible to find the perfect nanny, especially if you are not a millionaire. So I agreed to the bargain and awaited Hilda with a mixture of apprehension and relief.

She arrived with very little luggage, as she had left most of her property with Miss Mackey. But she did have a large photograph of a fluffy-haired woman with a pre-war look. She showed it with pride, adding to herself one more social honour. This was Dot, her youngest sister, who had trained as a nurse and been so brilliant that she had become a hospital matron in Sydney, Australia. Hilda hung the portrait on her bedroom wall. She also brought a few snapshots of the "little people" she had cared for in the past. They had, she said, loved their Hilda.

In the next weeks we were swamped with the gentry, Miss Mackey and "the doctor".

Hilda's father had been a small official in a coalmine, but she did not mention coal. Instead she dwelt on her prowess at school, where she reached the top grade at the age of twelve, and had won a prize for reciting poetry. She still liked to discuss poetry and instruct us. She told me that "Bobby" Burns was Britain's greatest poet. He was "Bobby" because Miss Mackey matily called him that, and to his greatness was added the fact that he was, like Miss Mackey, Scottish. Of course Miss Mackey knew everything about poetry.

When my boy was a little older Hilda presented him with R.L. Stevenson's *Child's Garden of Verse*. I was pleased that Paul should study poetry, but the illustrations were pretty but not quite "great". Hilda's learning did not include art.

She had hoped to be a teacher but her schooling came to a sudden end. She was the eldest of seven children, and she was twelve when her mother died. As she had reached the top grade at school she was allowed to leave, and she spent the rest of her youth bringing up her brothers and sisters. One by one they left the home, but old Mr Hudd remained and she looked after him till he died.

In those days there were few educational courses for the middle-aged, and Hilda had to swallow her pride and go into service. We never knew quite what she did except that it was with the gentry. I had missed them in my youth, but now I had them in full force. Hilda's tales reminded me of Jane Austen – with large houses and the

36

servants forming a world on their own.

When the family went visiting, Hilda said, they would take servants with them, and these joined the home below-stairs group. Each group would boast of its employers, trying to outdo the other. Hilda herself continued this gentry-boasting. When I once said something about brushing down the stairs she replied caustically that the gentry did not brush their stairs every day.

But the uneducated servants must have irked her. Once, she said, she had lent a book of poetry to a fellow maid. The maid did not return it nor comment, and Hilda said nothing either. But one day when the maid was out Hilda raided her room and found the book under a chamber pot. She took the book away and said nothing, and the girl also said nothing.

Somehow Hilda graduated to the post of nanny, and it was true that she linked well with children. Her "little people" with their snapshots formed another mark of superiority.

But her greatest glory was her acquaintance with Miss Mackey and "the doctor". How she had found work with this noble pair we never heard, but they had become her life and her greatest honour. The friend who had introduced us to Hilda had met the doctor and said he seemed a mild, little insignificant man, but to Hilda he was God. She told us how he had a canary which he fed on some kind of breakfast food, and she suggested that my boy should have it too. The doctor had a wonderful head of pure white hair, and he kept it so beautiful by washing it each morning in cold water. Hilda suggested that the same treatment might suit my Paul, but I did not take the hint.

The doctor was now a saint in heaven, but Miss Rowena Mackey remained. She was small and stocky with a protruding jaw, her face a little like an amiable cow's. But Hilda said she had had a scintillating girlhood, with dozens of marriage proposals. A millionaire had wanted to marry her. At another time we heard that she had been a brilliant musician and could have become a professional pianist if she had wished. She had a great knowledge of literature and had taught for years at Hellebore Girls' School where she was much honoured.

Miss Mackey had strong ideas about the education of children. One of her strongest beliefs was that football was an evil game because it exercised the legs but not the rest of the body. Hilda hoped that my Paul would never play football.

Miss Mackey called her teacher colleagues by their surnames; so Hilda did the same. She would casually mention Porter, Jones or MacNaughton. Sometimes she was invited to entertainments at the school and would return with satisfaction to announce that she had sat next to Porter or had a nice talk with MacNaughton. But Miss Mackey was always "Miss".

I have thought since that it was quite understandable that Hilda should suffer from "nerves". A life in which you are continually considered of a lower status than you deserve would inflame many souls, and Hilda's soul was often feverish. All the same her outbursts made affection difficult. She would flare up about nothing, make wild accusations, rush to her room and emerge next morning red-eyed and subdued.

Once it was about preserved eggs. In those days, before universal refrigeration, we used the treacly chilly liquid waterglass to preserve eggs, buying them cheap in summer and storing them for the expensive winter. Fishing in the gluey liquid one morning, I innocently remarked that I had thought we had more eggs left. At this Hilda turned on me and shouted that I was accusing her of being a thief, was I?

At another time there was an explosion when I asked her – timidly I am sure – not to put quite so much polish on the linoleum as I had slid over several times. I would do my best to avoid these outbreaks, which occurred every few weeks, but nothing could stop them.

Hilda had other peculiarities. One was her poor sense of time. My last sight of her was at Waterloo Station in London – a chance meeting. She said she had come to say goodbye to a sister but had arrived an hour late, not found the sister and now did not know whether to wait or not. And several times on a summer evening I arrived home from work to find a shut and deserted house with no indication of where she and the child might be. An hour later she would come hurrying in with the push-chair and the child who had not had his tea. She had, she would say, walked further than she intended and not noticed that it was so late.

I suppose it was increasing years that had deprived Hilda of any sense of smell. It is a sense that one can generally manage without; and Hilda did. But now and then there were crises. Once when I was away at work Hilda was energetically mopping the floor. A bowl electric fire had been pushed out of the way against the side of my desk, and with the mop Hilda hit the low switch and turned the fire on. Unaware, she continued to mop until she noticed a haze arising in the room. It would not go away, and she thought it was coming from beneath the floor. In the end she went in next door to ask if there was a haze there too. And the man of the house came back with her to investigate. He told me afterwards that the desk had been about to burst into flame.

It was a very glum Hilda who reported the accident to me that evening. She hated anything that decreased her image. I almost felt like apologising myself. There was a great charred patch on the side of the desk; so I claimed insurance. I received two pounds – quite a substantial sum in those days. But the smell of smoke hung about the house for days.

Hilda did actually cause the destruction of one of the most popular members of the household. Quackie was a stout upstanding small rubber duck with blue trousers and red buttons. One morning Hilda was preparing dinner when a smell of burning rubber began to creep through the house. There must be some electrical fault, I thought, and I went round examining cables, but could find nothing. I grew anxious, thinking that fire might break out at any moment. In the kitchen Hilda was tranquilly cutting up vegetables, yet the smell was suffocating there. The smell took me to the oven, and as I opened it a blast of heat and overpowering smell met me. At the bottom was a small colourless melting lump. It was almost liquid, but a faint streak of blue showed it was the former Quackie. I dropped it into cold water, but it was no good. Quackie had gone, and there remained only a sticky lump. It had to go into the dustbin.

The oven door must have been ajar and Paul for some unknown reason must have slipped Quackie inside. Hilda had not noticed and had blithely turned on the heat, and had then not noticed the smell. As usual she was hurt in her dignity, and became dumb and offended. I was more affected than Paul at Quackie's loss. When I asked him a year or two later if he remembered the duck he did not know what I was talking about.

I wonder now that I did not worry more over Hilda's accidents, but they occur in every household and with us they did not occur all the time. Also she got on well with Paul, playing with him with a nervous intensity and showing off her ability to enter a child's world. And I had read that changes upset children, and so time went on.

But then an unexpected event changed the situation.

First we heard a small report that Miss Mackey was not well. Then she was said to have cancer and then not to have many months to live. She was, it was reported, meeting her fate with great courage. She said, "I've never done anything wrong. So why should I be afraid to die?" If this showed a certain complacency, she was, as Hilda had told us many times, a paragon.

Through the illness Hilda displayed a grave dignity. The nervous outbreaks disappeared, and she remained quiet and self-contained. One could not say, of course, that she was enjoying the tension, but she was living up to it, herself the centre of tragedy.

After Miss Mackey's death Hilda went up and down to the "posh" house helping a distant cousin to clear up. She had become a person of importance and it suited her. And then, after all the years of drudgery, Hilda became what she had always longed to be – a person superior in the eyes of society.

Miss Mackey had always promised, it appeared, to leave her money so that she could visit Dot, the hospital matron in Australia. Now, when the will was read, if was found that Miss Mackey, who had no close relatives, had been better than her word. She had left the "posh" house to Hilda so that she could sell it and use the money to travel. After that Hilda became busy with solicitors and financial advisers.

We had to get a new nanny of course, but Hilda visited us. She remained instructive, telling us that Australia was a country noted for kangaroos and Australian winter was our summer etc. At least the details were new to Paul. She told the neighbours of her elevation and they said to me that Miss Hudd had always been a pleasant-spoken person.

She decided to travel as soon as possible. She bade the child a slightly emotional farewell, but he seemed to miss her less than I expected.

When she left, peace unutterable descended on the household. I arranged that my next help should come in daily.

After some weeks a letter arrived from Sydney written in a round old-fashioned hand. Hilda had arrived safely and was seeing her matron sister. Letters continued to come at intervals, and at Christmas Hilda sent cards to two neighbours as well as to us. Finally she announced that she was settling in Australia near her sister. The continent, of course, had few gentry and she was as good as anyone else.

She bought a handy little bungalow in a suburb. The road boasted several "little people" who were now coming to her gate and calling "Hilda. Hilda" as children had done in the old days in England.

And still Miss Mackey ruled. Hilda called her bungalow "Dunedin" after Miss Mackey's "posh" house. She had brought seed out from the garden and she sowed it and some of it germinated. She sent her respects to the old teacher friends – Porter, Jones and MacNaughton.

The letters continued for a few years. Then we had a note in an unknown hand. Miss Hudd had passed away after a short illness. It was cancer. She had followed Miss Mackey to the end.

Those last few years, when she was a person of some consequence, may have been among the happiest of Hilda's life. We hoped that she was now in a world where it did not matter if one was gentry or not.

# CHAPTER 7

# Nature. The Post was a Poplar.

We are in great confusion over "Nature". On the one hand we destroy it every day; on the other we feel it has some divine creation which brings us pleasure and peace. And, as we have discovered more and acquired new powers this century, the confusion has grown, with guilt and fear added. In the past nature seemed limitless even if we attacked it. Now we have a vision of a small world being destroyed by a plague of people. Prophecies of over-population and the total destruction of wild life chill us.

But that is not all. Nature itself has turned out to be not what we thought. It is not a Garden of Eden but a ruthless battle-ground. Every creature is fighting for itself, destroying without pity. Volcanoes and hurricanes have always been killers but now we find trees of the tranquil woodland, the wide-eyed daisy in the grass, as well as tigers and lions, are out to increase their kind at the expense of others. It is we who have the pity; they have none.

Oddly this has gone with a decay of formal religion, and serious people, mainly young, are trying to make a god of nature. Emotion is stronger than reason, and they talk proudly of the marvels of the "food chain" even though they know that it is founded on death and fear. Their own "conservation" efforts themselves entail destruction. Two boys I know joined a "conservation" party and were asked to cut down young birches to preserve heathland. They said that they preferred birches to heath and did not go again.

I once asked a conservationist if it was really necessary for small parties to visit small sites to hack down the brilliant wild mauve rhododendron, a favourite victim, or change tree shapes by coppicing. Could not Nature be left to itself a little? He replied that we have been interfering for thousands of years and we cannot stop now.

Among all the contradictions two certainties may remain. We are part of the struggle, and even while we worship the "green world" we destroy it when it stands in our way. At the same time Nature does bring a feeling of richness in spite of its cruelty.

I liked my poplars and hated to destroy them, but I destroyed them all the same. At the same time even a small suburban garden gave a feeling of richness.

I had bought my house partly because of the small Lombardy poplars planted closely to fringe front and back gardens. They had looked countrified and charming with their thin bare pink shoots twining in the soft December sun. I did not at the time ask why they were there, but I learnt afterwards that they had been planted as a barrier against the next-door family. There had been a quarrel, and presumably the poplars had been chosen because they grow quickly. But few people in their senses would have selected ranks of the tallest trees (potentially) in the country to screen the small garden of a terrace house. Our predecessor had not been a tree expert.

When we arrived the poplars, still only about eight feet tall, were hiding the road in front and the spreading red roofs at the back. But we hardly noticed them at first. We were busy settling down, and it was winter. And when spring came they were still pretty with their translucent gold little leaves. In summer the breeze gently ruffled the dark green foliage, and in autumn the leaves changed to bright yellow and black, and fell to make clear colour on the wet emerald grass.

But we slowly realised that the house was not getting much sun. In the back garden the rambler roses were pale and spindly and appeared later than usual in the season. The grass grew thin and the soil poor, and in winter the gardens were ankle-deep in leaves which turned to slime. And the poplars went up and up.

We tried to keep them down. Several times our odd-job man came and sawed off the central stems. But the outer branches curled over them and they went up as before. We felt as if we were living in a wood.

We liked our trees, and they gave the garden distinction, but in the end we realised that they could not continue. One Sunday morning our odd-job man came early and spent the day cutting them down in sections and digging out the roots. Front and back gardens were thick with leafy boughs which seemed to take up much more space than when they were on the trees. I found the operation painful, but the children were excited, jumping about among the leaves.

43

Our odd-job man cleared up well, piling the leaves at the bottom of the garden to dry for a bonfire and taking the stems home for pea-sticks. He sawed up the trunks for fuel in the open fires that we still possessed, and we burnt most of them though we found that poplar burns badly, making smoke and deadening the flames.

Meanwhile our garden had lost its distinction and looked like all the other small plots along the row with their concrete paths and brief patches of grass. And light beamed on us, making a different world. The traffic whirred outside, and at the back the small houses sprang at us. All the windows seemed to be staring, and the next door neighbours, we imagined, were looking straight down at our daily activities. I had the sad feeling that the change was irreversible. We could never bring our poplars back.

But I was wrong.

I wanted a post for my washing line, and I chose a spot on the back lawn, near where a poplar had been. There were still a few poplar scraps at the end of the garden, and our odd-job man made a post from a dry piece of branch, removing a few withered twigs and shaving it smooth. He hammered it in, and it made a solid post about five and a half feet high, and I stretched my line across to it from the yard.

I used the line comfortably for a few weeks. Then one morning I found a tiny leaf coming from the post, and broke if off and thought no more of it. A week later a tiny twig appeared a little farther up, and then another higher still. Then I had the impression that the post was higher than I had thought. The next twig that appeared was beyond by reach, and then is was quite clear that the post was growing. I stopped hanging my line on it, and the odd-job man fixed a solid concrete post in the yard.

Left to itself the poplar post developed with surprising rapidity. Branches grew from the top, and it took on the familiar paint-brush shape of Lombardy poplars. Years went on, and from my bedroom window I began to look into a bower of leaves. In storms the green tree swayed to and fro and seemed as if it might heel over, but we were told that poplar roots go deep and there was no danger. In the long midsummer twilights our back garden, seen from a downstairs window, seemed full of green light.

Then the poplar soared above the roof and became visible among the small houses. When I got off the bus I could see it ahead on the other side of the road, and I would wonder if there was any penalty for letting trees grow too large. It seemed like a tall plant in a small pot.

In the usual way we had the centre lopped, and in the usual way the branches curved round it, and it continued to go up. And in the usual way it ruled the garden.

The grass and plants thinned. Poplar roots began to appear in the flower beds, and the giant shadow fell across several gardens so that I was afraid of complaints.

Yet it was a magnificent tree, far above any of the trees around. "You won't get rid of it, will you?" a visitor said one June night when we stood under it and it pointed up to the stars.

"Never," I said.

But then came a long very dry summer. Birches and other shallow-rooted trees turned tawny and died, but still the poplar flourished with its spire of dark green leaves. But then, after a time, cracks began to appear in the concrete of our yard, and the outside lavatory began to slope. The poplar roots were underneath sucking away the moisture and they were still growing. They might undermine the house and neighbouring houses, advisers said. My elder boy remarked sarcastically that he did not want to be sued by neighbours after my death. I hesitated, and the lavatory sloped more. So, with great unwillingness, I did what I had sworn not to do and destroyed my last poplar.

A tree expert came and sawed the great tree down in segments. Again the back garden was full of tumbled leafy branches, and all that was left was a large flat circle of wood about an inch above the ground. It would be too difficult, the tree man said, to dig it out. "I expect it will die anyhow. If not, I'll come back and deal with it."

But I might have known. The poplar would not die. In a week a fringe of fine twigs and leaves began to appear round the edge of the wooden circle, and grew rapidly. We were beginning to have another poplar tree.

It could not go on. I summoned the tree man, and he poured poison over the stump. "I've put a sheet of glass over it so it won't hurt the cats," he said agreeably. I knew nothing then about garden poisons, and I hope not to know any more.

The garden became sick. It seemed as if the poplar was having its revenge, but of course trees do not have human feelings. The fringe of leaves round the stump withered and died in a few days, and the roots round the garden disappeared. But then the stems of the peony near by blackened, thinned and drooped, and the flowers mouldered. It took three years for the plant to recover. An apple tree next door died, and then the hedges began to shrivel and go brown. It seemed that the effect of the poison would last for ever.

We asked for advice and were told that we now had the dreaded honey fungus – the growth that is beneficial in woods, destroying the remains of dead trees and enriching the soil, but is deadly in gardens. It took months of digging privet bushes out and disinfecting before we seemed safe. But the hedges were never the same again and we still got unexpected deaths among plants.

Yet, strangely, the struggle with the poplars left a final impression of the green world's richness – the feeling I had had when I found the first signs of life in the washing post. The tree man had left two great segments of poplar trunk at the end of the garden – standing upright so that they could accumulate a covering of dust and dead leaves. They stood through the winter, and in spring I noticed clusters of budding plants growing over them. They were blue columbines. We had a few columbine plants in the garden, and these must have seeded, but those growing out of the logs were larger and deeper in colour and lasted longer than the garden ones. I watered them, and they were there for weeks – the dark decaying logs and the blue flowers waving above them.

The poisoned wooden circle left in the ground slowly powdered away until after a few years it became part of the soil, only looser. One day a tuft of bracken appeared growing out of it – a gift from the birds, I suppose, as we do get many unexpected plants appearing suddenly in this close group of gardens on the edge of the country.

I had set a few small snowdrop plants at the end of the garden. One spring I noticed to my surprise a large clump flowering in the middle of the old stump. It must have seeded from the others, though it was some distance away. The clump was larger and the flowers taller and more abundant than the others. They have continued.

# CHAPTER 8
## *Money Matters. Spending and Owing*

Money has been one of the chief preoccupations of the twentieth century, and it still is – the subject of international debate and endless personal conversations touched with pride or envy. At the beginning of the century the "poor" were a recognised part of society. They lived in hovels, did menial jobs, and were dirty, with poor health and vulgar habits. At the end of the century the manual worker often earns more than the professional, and working-class families have modern homes full of new devices, with holidays in Benidorm. At the beginning of the century nobody thought of the incomes of the Royal Family and the Archbishop of Canterbury. At the end everybody's income is known and discussed.

When I came south from the Midlands at the end of the Second World War I was amazed at the way the previous "poor" were spending money. In the 1930s in Birmingham the poor lived in back-to-back houses in courts, sometimes with only one cold-water tap and a communal lavatory. Houses consisted of only a kitchen and a narrow stair leading up to a bedroom and attic. Walls were bug-infested; basements flooded. Workers received less than a living wage, and factories closed for an August week of stock-taking, but the employees were not paid. In winter the old would debate whether hunger or cold were worse, and would go to bed to keep warm or sometimes chop up furniture to make a fire.

Yet by then they were receiving a small Government pension – a few shillings a week – and would talk of the bad old days when they had no help at all. The general opinion was that people were kinder to one another when they were destitute, and certainly the poor have always helped one another more than the well-off have done.

But among all the washing machines and package holidays that I found after the war there were flaws. It was partly that people had had no experience of spending money prudently; partly there was so much more to buy. The churches were no longer preaching the virtues of humility and poverty, and people no longer went to church anyhow. Money became a symbol of success and happiness. People over-spent with their mortgages and freezers and then were desperately worried. The Offers, warm-hearted and generous as they were, had their life ruined by mismanagement of money.

I realised that first evening that we should be lucky if Eileen Offer came to us. She sat, dark-haired, open and friendly, in one of the boys' bedrooms with her tiny composed Shirl beside her. The two boys, after their bath, sat watching from a bed, and I noticed that Mrs Offer, instead of talking of herself, enquired about them.

The Offers had a flat above offices in the builder's yard down the road, and Stan Offer drove one of the lorries. Mrs Offer had come to discuss the job of looking after my boys. She wanted work in which she could keep Shirl, aged two, with her. "She is a very good little girl," Mrs Offer said, "and knows all her nursery rhymes." Mrs Offer added that she herself was not an expert cook but could do good plain cooking. This proved true.

I felt cheerful after I had concluded the arrangement. It had never been easy to find suitable help in an area which had factory and shop jobs available, and this seemed the most satisfactory arrangement that I had yet had. The boys liked Mrs Offer too.

Her husband Stan turned out to be equally agreeable. He had a spare boyish figure, close-cut hair and a merry look, and we heard later that he had been brought up in a charity home which gave him an aura of respectability. He seemed on good terms with everybody and addressed strangers as "brother". He told me that all his carpentry tools had gone, as he had lent them to acquaintances and had not had them back. He had a car and gave lifts to strangers, and once, when he had a free afternoon, he drove my boys two miles to the station to meet me as I came from work. Six times a year he drove a young cousin to and from boarding school thirty miles away. He, of course, provided the petrol.

At that time, in the 'fifties', it was the custom, when you met a pram in the street, to press a penny into the hand of the infant. Mrs Offer gave shillings, not pennies. Then, when friends of hers were expecting a child, she gave them all Shirl's baby clothes though she was still hoping for another infant of her own. Stan took the baby clothes to the family forty miles away. "And they didn't even suggest paying for the petrol," Mrs Offer told me.

Shirl used to bring expensive toys for my boys to see, and she was being educated to be as generous as her parents. One Monday Mrs Offer told me with pride, "Shirl was such a good little girl yesterday. Some friends came to tea. Well, they aren't too clean, and he drinks a bit. But I like to make them a nice meal when they look in. And Shirl gave the little girl her dolls' pram."

I had heard of the dolls' pram. It had been a birthday present, and the Offers had spent more on it than I should have dreamed of spending. Now it had gone as easily as it had come. "Wasn't it a kind thing to do?" Mrs Offer said. "We've promised to buy her another."

I came to the conclusion that Stan was earning very high wages or that the Offers had some private income. I relied on Mrs Offer more and more. She was capable, open and easy, and she was good to the boys.

And then one morning she arrived red-eyed. She was holding a local paper. "I got this for Stan," she said.

I thought that Stan must want to read the local news, although the Offers already spent a good deal on popular papers. But she said in a tearful way, "I thought there might be some job for him, but there's nothing."

I did not understand. Stan already had a job.

"I was going to give you notice," Eileen explained, "and Stan would give notice at the yard." A tear dropped. Shirl looked up but remained quiet. Eileen pulled out a handkerchief and muttered something about not being shamed.

There was all the morning work to be done, and I had to go to London. But we spent almost an hour, and other hours afterwards, untangling the Offers' life story. Eileen was a good talker.

Eileen had been born in the East End of London. But she had plenty of fun, she said. She remembered particularly the ornaments on the mantelpiece of their upstairs lodging. Mum had two china dogs and two china baskets of flowers, and she loved those ornaments and was always washing them.

Mum had married young and had a drunken husband, with eight children, though two had died. Then the husband died too, and

Mum was free. But she went and married again, and this husband, Eileen's father, was a worse drinker than the other. Seven children came by the second marriage, and Eileen was the youngest.

The first family had gone, and Eileen knew little of them. Of her own brood two girls had weak hearts, and they went into some home and never came back. But Eileen kept in touch with a brother and with a sister who had married at seventeen and already had four children.

In her easy way Eileen laughed over her childhood. It was often uncomfortable, but there were a lot of them together, and Mum was good. The worst trouble was Dad. They would be at dinner round the table, and his step would be heard on the stairs. Mum would shush them. "Not a word," she would say, and they would all sit quiet with their eyes cast down. But that didn't make any difference to Dad. He would start roaring, and somebody would be hit or a piece of furniture broken.

Worst was one Christmas Day, Mum had worked hard to get a nice Christmas dinner together, and when Dad came in it was on the table. He seized the dishes and pitched them at the wall. The dinner was lost and the room so messed up that you couldn't stay there. Without saying anything Mum just bundled the children into a neighbour's, and there they had to stay while she cleaned up.

Dad worked on casual jobs but only now and then. In between times he would sit by the fire while Mum worked. She would take any kind of job, and if there was nothing she sold flowers in the street. Then she had the little ones with her out of Dad's way. Dad would wait till she came back, and then use her money for a drink.

But there was plenty of fun. On Saturday evenings Mum cooked chips in the old black pan, and they had a hot supper. Then the war came, and there were more jobs about, and Mum was not as worried about money. The family was growing up, and Eileen herself was at school. This, she thought, was nice because the sirens were always sounding, and the children went down to the air-raid shelter and didn't have to learn anything. But she was always afraid that the sirens would go when she was about in the street.

I asked her why she had not been evacuated, but she did not seem to have heard of the idea. She admitted that she had not learnt much in those days of air-raids, and now in her late twenties she could not write very well. But she could do family shopping, though her muddles over money may have been partly due to lack of practice with figures. She could read enough to enjoy popular papers and she could remember well. Her reminiscences entertained me for weeks.

Eileen began to earn wages before the end of the war. She seemed to have had no difficulty in finding jobs in those days of shortage of labour. Even after the war, when there were redundancies, she drifted quite easily from one job to another. In her early twenties she was a forewoman in a tailoring business and earning nearly ten pounds a week – an unusual sum for an uneducated girl. But she did not save much.

"The girls ran sweepstakes," she said. "And sometimes I'd have a week-end at the seaside with a friend, and I'd spend about twenty pounds. Then there was the money you had to hand back to the Government." She did not understand about that. Anyhow at the end of the week she was often nearly broke.

And then coupons were abolished, and she liked to spend money on clothes. Nylon stockings were coming in from America, and all the girls wanted them. And, of course, nobody in her family had ever saved anything.

"I was always laughing in those days," Eileen said. "The girls used to declare that I'd never get married because I was not serious enough and had too many fellows."

She had reached the advanced age of twenty-two when Stan came along. He was a driver but had no family and was lonely; so they spent a good deal of time together. She did not think much about the future, but one day he said, "When is it to be?" And, still not thinking much, she said, "You'd better ask Dad."

I heard from both of them separately about the wedding, and each implied that the other had been extravagant. Eileen had managed to save £150, and expected to spend it on setting up the home after a register-office ceremony. But Stan suggested a church wedding, and she agreed to please him. But Stan told me that Eileen had hankered after a "white wedding," though neither attended church, and he did as she wished. All her savings went on the church ceremony.

Stan said too that he had been amazed at the way she went from shop to shop ordering goods on the "never-never". But they were

51

both working, and he had expected that they would pay off the debts quite soon. Their early married life was light-hearted. He would leave her notes asking if he might bring a friend home to supper, and she had somehow learned to cook and made nice meals to please him, and they would be happy.

They began to pay off their debts. But then she had a terrible shock. She was pregnant. She had seen plenty of the problems that babies can bring, and she did not particularly want children of her own. "I thought Stan would've murdered me," she said.

Both parents now loved little Shirl, but she had been one of the causes of their troubles. The women of Eileen's world had always worked to the last moment of the pregnancies, and she had expected to do the same. Her firm wanted to keep her and offered maternity leave; so she bought expensive baby clothes on the "never-never", and continued to work till the eighth month. Then she climbed on to a chair to get a saucepan and fell. So Shirl was born a month early.

"And oh," Eileen said, "I did think she was a terrible little thing. She was so tiny I was afraid to bath her in case she went down the plug-hole."

Eileen's acquaintances always went back to work after a birth, and Eileen expected to go back too. But the hospital kept her in for ten days because of complications, and she worried that Stan was spending too much money. Her worries had begun even while she spent recklessly herself. When she came out of hospital she arranged for a neighbour to look after the baby, but she offered the woman two pounds a week – more than was usually paid in those days – and this ate into her wages.

And, though I did not know it at the time, Eileen never stayed in a job for long. And winter was coming, and the child had to be taken out early in the morning. The neighbour was kind, but Eileen did not think she was very clean. So she decided to look after Shirl herself for a while and gave up a good job.

From that time troubles rolled on the Offers. Eileen was not used to managing on one man's wage, and she wanted everything of the best for the baby. Their action over an insurance scheme that they had entered at marriage was typical. They had paid for only a year and ten months, but if they had continued for two years they would have got some of their money back. But they did not think of that; ceased to pay two months too soon, and lost all their payments – something over twenty pounds.

Stan, with his "home" bringing up, also seemed helpless over money matters. "Well," Eileen said to me, "we haven't yet paid for all the furniture, and there are the bills for Shirl's things." She was still spending lavishly on the child's clothes though not on her own. Stan was earning only nine pounds a week, and both of them smoked heavily. When I once said that, if I were in debt, I should give up smoking, Eileen replied reproachfully, "But a man must have his pleasures."

I heard no more of Dad, but Mum was still living in London. Eileen visited her each week-end and took a Sunday joint. "Mum will have the *best* meat," she said.

She had tried to stave off creditors by paying one or two a little each week and promising more. But at the end of the week there was nothing left. Stan would rush in with his wages on Friday half an hour before the shops closed, and Eileen would rush out to buy necessities – always in small quantities so that she paid more for the food. By Monday there was hardly any money left. Even when she was earning wagers from me she would show her empty purse and say laughing," Roll on the week-end." And by Thursday, she told me, all they had to eat was potatoes.

Finally, she said, they had to escape. They had seen an advertisement for a builder's driver at Redbury, and Stan had applied. The wage was a little less than in London and they would be farther from Mum, but they would be away from the collectors. Not that Eileen wanted to be dishonest. She had given some of the firms her new address. But in any case she did not think reasonably. She kept saying, "I just had to get away."

Then another trouble arose. Stan was "mad" on cars, and his boss suggested that he should have one of his own. The boss would buy the car and pay for it by taking a little from Stan's wages each week. Stan did not like to refuse, and so his wages went down again. The boss bought a second-hand car which kept on going wrong, and Stan tinkered with it and made it worse. So repair bills were added to tax and petrol.

Now Eileen had received a threatening demand note from one of the London creditors, and she was terrified. She foresaw prison, and said that the Police would be called in and she would be "shamed".

Yet her mind still seemed in separate compartments. After crying and saying that she had been awake all night, she would tell me that she was thinking of arranging dancing lessons for Shirl. "I don't suppose they'll cost more than a few guineas."

But that morning when she came in crying she was bent on another escape. She wanted to go to the Isle of Wight. Why the Isle of Wight? She didn't really know. Only people had said that it was nice there and the residents were kind. But she had looked in the paper and there was no mention of the Isle of Wight and no suitable job anywhere else. She was in despair.

But I wanted her to stay with me. We had grown fond of her, and she was a comfortable person to have in the home. So I finally suggested that she should reckon up her debts and I would pay them, and she would pay me back in work.

Eileen was immediately joyful and full of plans for the future. She had no idea how much she owed, but she brought along a collection of grubby bills and paying books, and I pored over them, sometimes contacting the firms. It turned out that she owed something over a hundred pounds, quite a large sum for those days but hardly one to cause so much misery. I paid the money and gave Eileen a receipt for her work each week.

It was not easy. I was often tempted to forgive her the debt, for she needed her wages. Perhaps I should have released her from the arrangement, but she was still doing reckless things with Stan's small income. So I stuck to the bargain.

Excellent help as she was, her own disasters continued. She bought an expensive oil stove, saying that it had to be expensive because you could not get a cheap one with hire purchase. I objected to her return to hire purchase, but she said they had to be warm, hadn't they? And her flat was damp. And then, long before she had paid for the stove, it flared up and set fire to her curtains. She was afraid to use it again, and she had to get new curtains.

She was cheated over a television set – a long complicated story. Then Stan had an accident with his car while he was still paying for it. Then Eileen's Mum died, and Eileen spent what seemed to me a huge sum on a floral arrangement called "The gates of heaven".

It took her a long time to pay off her debt in work, for sometimes she just had to have some money. But she came in regularly and finally she was free – to my own relief. "You musn't think," she said earnestly, "that I shall leave you when I've worked if off."

I had not thought it. She seemed part of the household. But then she did leave me. She was tired of a domestic job and thought that she would like to work in a shop. I tried to persuade her to stay, but it was no good. She had never worked anywhere for long. But she said she would visit us.

She found a shop job quite easily. But the hours were long, and she had to leave Shirl with an acquaintance. She worked for about two months, paid off some new debts and then gave the job up. She had a break, and then went out cleaning – for another few months.

She came to see us once or twice, always bringing presents. Once it was apples that a friend had given her. It also seemed possible that the Offers were growing more prudent. Eileen announced that Stan was getting rid of the car which had become "a real old crock". A garage had said that repairs would cost £30. "Well, we haven't got the money. So Stan's sold it for £25. That will help to pay the other debts."

By this time Stan had paid for the car and was receiving a full wage. But then he himself decided to move. Eileen gave various reasons – a stingy boss, a damp flat, lorries dangerous to Shirl – but really, of course, they wanted a change again. Stan got a job some miles away, and they moved and stopped coming to see us. For a year or two we lost touch with them.

Then one afternoon I ran into Eileen and Shirl in a greengrocer's some way down the road. Eileen said that they were living in a flat in a side road near by. Shirl had become a lanky child of six, and had lost some of her doll-like charm, but she still gave the impression of a good little girl, and she was dressed in a spotless blue coat. Eileen said that she was doing well at school.

Eileen herself was pregnant – to hew own surprise. She had told me in the past that she wanted "another nipper", but nothing had happened. "It's my nerves," she said. She had, even while she was crying over her debts, thought of adopting a child as a companion for Shirl. Now there would be no need.

She was very cheerful. Stan liked his job though it was some way away and the fares were heavy and he got home late. She herself had a job of cleaning at a hairdresser's. "I'll keep it up as long as I can," she said in her easy way. "I've got another five months to go, and I shan't be big. I'm too skinny". She promised to let me know when the baby arrived.

Stan rang me up in the winter and said she had had a boy. It had been a difficult labour, and Eileen had developed bronchitis afterwards, but she was better now, and Shirl had been a great help. "She isn't half delighted," Stan said.

And they were not much in debt. Eileen had paid for the baby clothes with her cleaning wages. Would I come and see them?

That last meeting will always leave a memory of comfort. It was a cold afternoon, but up some stairs I found Eileen sitting in an armchair by a bright fire. She was pale but had the good looks of new motherhood. Shirl was on the floor beside her with a book. The room was warm with red curtains and a pot of tea on the table.

I was given tea and home-made cake and then was taken into the bedroom to see the new baby. The pram and blankets were new and expensive-looking. The infant was dark-haired, small and sallow, but Eileen said he was the spit of Shirl at that age, and she got out some snapshots to prove it. Then we nursed the baby in front of the fire, while Stan cleared away the cups. He and Eileen now seemed very fond of one another. Life had turned out well for them after all.

They had asked me to come again, but I did not hear, and I was busy and the months went by. It must have been nearly a year later when the telephone rang one evening.

"How are you stranger?"

"Eileen?"

"Yes. Me again. I wondered if you'd come and see us. We've moved again. We're in Ealing."

"How are you getting on?"

"Fine."

"And the family and Stan?"

"Fine too. But he's changed his job again."

"Oh dear."

"You come and see us, and I'll tell you all about it... The new job's further away. Costs a good deal in travel."

Silence for a moment. Then she said timidly, "I been to four money-lenders this evening, but not one was any good."

I suppose I sighed, and she heard.

"It's the rent," she said hurriedly. "I been to my sister as well. She owes me a lot of money, but she can't pay me back. All them children. She bought a diamond ring on the never-never, so she could sell it and pay some debts, but now she can't pay for the ring installments. And my brother owes me money too, but he's left his first wife and now he has two homes to pay for... Could you" – and then in a rush – "Could you lend me thirty pounds?"

So they had not settled down after all. I did not want to embark on more money transactions, but Eileen was tearful with worry. We finally arranged some deal, but I was too busy to make the journey to visit her. So she began to pay me back, two pounds at a time, by post.

She did it in the most wasteful manner possible, ringing up from a public telephone box to say that the money was coming, and then buying a postal order and sending it by registered post.

This went on for a month or two, and then there was a gap, another payment and then another gap.

And then the Offers vanished.

# CHAPTER 9

# Education and Waste. Sue Grows Up.

When I remember Sue Baker with her straight bobbed hair and rosy face she seems too insignificant to represent the century. But she was important for a time to a small group of children, and she did represent the rather poor education of the masses just after the war. But we are all influenced by many things, and Sue also reflected an unsympathetic home and the passions of adolescence.

Talent, of course, has always been wasted among humble people. When I settled at Redbury I noticed that here and there were people who should have been actors, singers, artists. But by family tradition they had left school at fourteen and become road workers or machine-minders. A woman housekeeping for me for a short time had a clever son who excelled in examinations, obviously material for a university, but his father was a milkman and did not believe in higher education. He insisted that the boy should leave school at sixteen, and the boy himself wanted to leave to be like his mates and earn money. So he left and disappeared into the anonymous labour market.

There may be less waste now than before, but it seemed to me in the mid century that the children of the masses were being shovelled through a system that gave some basic training but, when the clever ones had been skimmed off, provided little to interest the remaining adolescents. Towards the end of the school course pupils like Sue Baker were just marking time till they could escape.

Education is not everything, and Sue had the advantage of a cheerful temperament. Later she achieved two husbands and three children. All the same she could have done a little more with her sweet voice and drawings of chocolate-box ladies.

Sue did not seem to have any parents. She lived with an aunt in one of the small houses bordering the back alley, and there was gossip about some man living there too. We got to know her when my elder boy was six and she was ten, and she declared that she was going to marry him. She was already looking for opportunities for advancement, and she was fond of my boys for a time. But in the end she abandoned us.

At the age of ten she looked an ordinary child with black plimsoles, a gym dress and straight short hair held by a slide. Her aunt, a neat little woman who worked in a shop, left her much alone, with hours to kill at week-ends. The aunt was very affable when one met her, but she was reputed to "lead Sue a life", shouting at her and not troubling how the girl spent her spare time.

For years Sue's spare time was spent in the alley or with us. The neighbours patronised her and sometimes gave her crisps or biscuits, and we did too. She devoured everything offered, and dropped the papers in the alley. She certainly had a large appetite. Once when I was busy I gave her an unopened packet of biscuits, thinking she would take one or two, but later I found the empty carton dropped on our lawn. She had eaten all the biscuits.

Sometimes she asked for more than biscuits. A neighbour told me that Sue had knocked on her door one evening after dark. "Auntie says can she borrow sixpence?"

"Sixpence? What's she want sixpence for?"

"She just wants it," Sue was reported as saying. "She'll pay it back."

"Now, is it likely," the neighbour said to me, "that Mrs Price would send the girl across in the dark to borrow sixpence? I told her to get along."

Sue also manoeuvred for outings. She would play with the alley children, hear that a family was going out in the afternoon and whisper to the children that she wished that she could come too. Then she would be near the family gate and looking wistful when the group emerged, and a child would cry, "Can Sue come too?" She tried the technique on us when she began to know us, and it worked. But one must add that she was a pleasant lively companion, and it was no hardship to take her along if one could afford it.

Soon she was spending most of the week-end with us. She came in gradually. First she was making paper arrows for the boys to throw into our garden. Then she advanced to the old air-raid shelter which had not been taken away at the end of the war, and drew faces on the concrete in red chalk. Then she was on our lawn making daisy chains for the boys. Once when I was upstairs she picked all my best flowers and presented them to me when I came down. I did not know whether to thank her or be angry, but she smiled so sweetly that I had to thank her. Finally she was tapping on the back door every Saturday morning.

But I could never trust Sue. Once on a wet Saturday morning I went out shopping, leaving mid-morning lunch of biscuits and orange drink for her and the two boys. I returned to find that all the biscuits had gone and all the bananas from the bowl in the kitchen. The boys told me that Sue had said, "Now that *she's* out let's take what we want."

She devised, without asking me, the game of climbing onto the back of the settee in the front room and squeezing through the casement window behind. The boys were small and agile, but Sue was plump and no light weight, and the paint got scratched and the window was in danger. I was getting used to Sue by this time, and hearing the bumps and the laughter went to investigate and stopped it.

She was fond of aimlessly scraping and hammering on the concrete side of the old air-raid shelter, and drawing faces on flat parts. But her exploits in our outside lavatory were more spectacular. She got hold of some bright lemon-yellow paint and, while I was upstairs, persuaded the boys to help her paint the seat. Later she amused them by tearing up newspaper, strewing it about in the lavatory and throwing a lighted match among the pieces. There was a flare-up and the woodwork was singed.

She played with our radio and broke it and left it without confessing. When I scolded her she always said, "*He* told me to do it," he being Paul.

"You should ask me, Sue, not the boys."

She would smile sweetly, say nothing, and soon be inventing more mischief.

Soon she was having tea with us every week-end. She ate most of the cakes and drank most of the orange squash, but she had a curious habit of indicating that she wanted more drink. She would lift her empty glass to her lips and make loud sipping noises, and the boys would cry, "Sue wants more orange." But if she went on eating and drinking too long after they had finished they would plead, "Oh come on Sue." Then she would get up good-humouredly and carry the last chocolate cake into the garden.

We took her out most Saturdays, and she would run off afterwards without a thank-you. Her aunt did not apparently enquire what she had been doing. Once only, when we were making a long complicated bus trip to London Airport, did she bring her fare. The Airport had plenty of amusements for children, and I spent a good deal on a crowded afternoon and tea. Then a pleasure plane began to go up, taking visitors to circle over the Airport for ten minutes. The rides were not cheap, but the boys begged to go up. Sue as usual said nothing but looked wistful, gazing at the plane and gazing at me.

Of course the three of them went up in the end. Sue returned beaming but did not say thank-you. It had been an expensive afternoon, but we had enjoyed it and returned content. Only Sue became thoughtful in the home-going bus, and asked how much her fare had been each way. I worked it out, and she announced with a slightly aggrieved air, "You owe me a penny then."

She had her penny and took it home with the satisfied look of one who had obtained justice.


And yet, time and again, I was pleased to see Sue's brown bob coming up the back-garden path. The boys would be waiting for her and would open the door, and she would supply the morning's entertainment.

Early in our acquaintance she sent a note up by the boys: "Can I play on your pianow"? I consented, and she would come in and rattle away while the boys watched or danced. She had had no piano lessons, but she could play tunes by ear, adding dashing chords. Once I caught a Mozart air, and asked where she had picked it up. She had no idea what it was but said she had heard it at school.

Otherwise school did not seem to be teaching her much. Once she asked me what agriculture meant. I gave her a dictionary to look the word up. She fingered listlessly through the middle of the book; then threw it down.

Yet she was clever with her hands. She made paper lanterns as she had learned at school, using our coloured paper of course. She sent the boys to ask me to buy crepe paper, and then cut out hats and skirts and dressed them as princes. She raided our rag drawer to find pieces for trains and scarves, fixed them with safety pins and paraded the boys in front of our long hall mirror.

Once she dressed several of the alley children as kings and queens, using – without permission – tall plants from our garden as sceptres. One small girl had a dolls' pram, and Sue organised a mother-and-father game. Often she procured chalks and marked out a hopscotch game on the alley concrete. She did not clear up rubbish left by the games.

When bad weather kept them in she would get hold of the boys' paintbox, ask for paper and paint heads of girls in a chocolate-box style or cats, of which she was fond. I asked her if she had artists in her family, and she said she had an uncle who had made a fortune by designing Christmas cards but he had gone to America. One could not tell how much her stories were to be believed; not entirely I discovered.

She had a sweet singing voice, and would sing as she played the piano. She told me that she was one of the best singers in the school, and when she was fifteen she was going to Paris with a singing scholarship. Meanwhile she was going with a choir from school to sing to the Queen at Buckingham Palace. A neighbour whose child was also involved told me that this was really a trip to a London hall to sing in a youth festival.

When the time came for Sue's "eleven-plus" I asked her how she had got on, but she did not seem to know anything about the examination. Then she announced that her aunt was going to send her to college in London, but later she said that she was learning typing at school and was going to be a secretary to a large firm. Altogether, in spite of her stories, we concluded that her school was not doing a great deal for her.

At fourteen Sue began to develop an adolescent figure; to wear rings and bracelets and frizz her straight hair. She wore high-heeled slippers instead of plimsoles, with bright blouses and tight short skirts. For a time she tap-tapped up our garden path, but then her visits ceased, and the boys came up from the alley without her.

They began to play with children more of their own age, but they brought in various tales of Sue. One was that she had invited herself to a big boys' firework party and stayed till the early hours. Another was that she was getting engaged.

When I next saw her I hardly knew her. Her hair was red and a mass of curls. Her eyebrows were thickly pencilled black and her lips scarlet. She wore a short azure skirt and a cherry-red jacket, and she clicked along the street looking very pretty and about thirty. I could not tell if she saw me. Apparently not.

Later when I saw her by the shops her hair was orange, and as before she was dressed in brilliant colours. It was Monday morning, but a neighbour told me that Sue was leaving school at the end of the term and so was not bothering to go in much.

Once I passed her standing at a corner of the alley with two youths. She looked, as so often in our neighbourhood, of a higher type than the two spotty boys. The three were smoking cigarettes, saying nothing but gazing at one another and casting insolent glances at passers-by. Again she did not seem to know me.

This was before the boyfriend era, and early engagement and marriage were the goal of most girls. My boys said that Sue's fiancé was the lad who helped the milkman, and one Saturday we came across her with a spotty youth at the local railway station. They were sitting on a bench, holding hands and gazing into one another's eyes, unheeding of spectators. When the train came they avoided our compartment. My boys thought the youth was the milkman's lad but were not sure. Apparently after all Sue was still toying with lovers.

The neighbours told me later that Sue had been doing a few small jobs but had changed several times. Anyhow it did not matter as she was soon getting married. They added that she was "up to no good", always with a cigarette at the corner of her mouth. But they did not criticise for long for Sue's aunt moved, taking Sue with her, and we saw them no more.

It must have been ten years later when I met Sue's aunt in a bus. We were very affable as one is to an old acquaintance whom one has not seen for years. I asked after Sue and was given the surprising news that she was not only "very well" and "lovely", but she had had two husbands – with three children.

The first husband, Mrs Price said, had been devoted to her but had died. She did not say how. How had the amorous Sue coped with tragedy? It appeared that she did not need to cope. She had married again, and the second husband was as devoted as the first. She was very happy.

But what about the painting, the singing, the dressing-up? Presumably the talents had been lost, unless they were transmitted to those three children.

There is always hope in new lives – and perhaps in new education.

# CHAPTER 10

# Country to Suburb. Wildlife Mysteries

This century has had opportunities which no other century has had to the same extent – opportunities to study what wild creatures do when their fields and woods are built over. Suddenly the creatures' age-old environment has gone. Do they stay or go or die out?

This century – at least the second half of it – has also been unique in surveys of wild life. Month after month reports appear on birds (the favourites), mammals, insects and plants – their waxing or, more probably, waning. But no-one, it seems, has watched a change from country to housing settlement to see what has happened to the hedge-dwellers and field crawlers.

I have seen a housing estate grow over half a century, and the result has not been as simple as one might expect. The wild life did not just die out. Sometimes it prospered for a period. And the change has been not only in the building but in our own habits. Human life with its new machines has changed from last century's, and wild life has had to adapt to that too. And change is still going on. The impression has been of some fading out, adaptation and much mystery.

Fifty years ago our half-built suburb was very different. There were still waste patches of land where dogs could romp and "nature" do what it liked. The stream at the bottom of our valley was impeded by an old pram, a cycle wheel and boulders of concrete, but it still flowed openly. Fields and a small wood at the back were littered with old mattresses and rubbish, but some fields were still there. Large trees, horse chestnuts, oaks and elms, still stood in odd places. And our now unceasing two-lane road was only a narrow ribbon going out to fields. There was a general air of untidiness and unfinishedness, and the place suited some insects at any rate.

Flies buzzed at our windows and wove circles above our heads. In the new small kitchens sticky fly-papers hung with their dead and struggling victims. Domed meshed metal covers were placed over meat to keep the bluebottles out, but they sometimes got in and produced maggots. Flies bred in dustbins where old food mingled with the ashes from open fires. In summer our one cake-shop was full of dancing flies and wasps which settled on the "fancies" displayed bare; and the girls licked their thumbs and fingers to open paper bags for cakes. Bread was sold bare. Flies and wasps crawled over fish on the fishmonger's slab and over meat counters. One of the first words learnt by my elder boy was "fly".

Ants did well too. New gardens had concrete paths, and frost cracked the concrete. The cracks made admirable homes for ants, and most gardens had colonies of them. I shall never forget my first introduction to their armies. We had moved in winter and I was unprepared. I came down one May morning to find a dish of stewed cherries covered with a thick black crust, and ants crawling aimlessly on all the cupboard shelves. They had come up outside the pipes leading from the garden, and were also crawling on the floor and table. There were even some on a shelf far back by the inner door, though how they had reached it was a mystery.

At first I tried to brush them off and return them outside, but more and more came. Finally I washed thousands down the sink. I covered up all the food and hid it in the fridge, but they came for days. And I had to repeat the battle spring after spring.

But the May visitations were not all. In summer we used sometimes to sit on the kitchen steps which were sunny and gave us a view of the descending garden. In July we would feel a tickling under our knees and look down to find the brick steps crawling with excited ants while large winged queens soared into the air to mate. After the seething mass had emerged in several Julys I lost patience and poured boiling water into the cracks, hoping it would cause a quick death. The steps remained bare after that.

Gradually round the estate the ants subsided though one still hears of them sometimes. Like other insects they remain mysterious. Also mysterious were the woodlice, flat and brown, that clustered under flowerpots and bits of stone and wood, seeking damp places. Were they newcomers or had they been there when our land, before the building development, had been an orchard? Certainly they learnt a new trick in dry weather. We began to find them in ones and twos in different sizes, motionless, upstairs in our bathroom basin. They must have crawled up our waste-pipe to the cool damp porcelain. They remained unmoving day and night, and when I tried to flood one down it would crawl out of the plug-hole again a few minutes later. They seemed to live a death in life, but now they have gone, how and why we do not know.

Seasonal mysteries, of course, go on in all gardens. Suddenly an elder bush is covered with a blanket of blackfly or rosebuds covered with greenfly. Where were the thousands of insects yesterday? On an August morning after rain long flat slugs, orange or shining black, are in the wet grass. Or they have trailed across the front doorstep and chewed the paper note I put out for the milkman so that it is now unreadable lace. Where were they in the dry days before the rain?

In autumn suddenly small spiders are making webs in the hedges or across narrow paths. Where were they a week ago? And where were the great crab-like solitary spiders that scuttle across the floor on autumn evenings?

Wasps have waned with refrigeration, pesticides and only a few small fruit trees in the new gardens. Butterflies, like birds, wax and wane, and when they wane the public is blamed. We are bidden to plant buddleias and other butterfly-attractive plants in our gardens; and the butterflies are coming back, but generally in Redbury we see the graceful cabbage white, flickering round and looking for a vegetable patch to ruin our brassicas. It is a pity that butterflies have to be preceded by caterpillars.

We understand why the dragonflies that used to dance against our windows have gone. The stream at the bottom of our dip has been culverted, and only a dry streak of clay now marks its piped course. We understand why bumblebees rather than honeybees are in our gardens. The people who came out to Redbury were mainly town-dwellers and did not keep bees, and have not begun now. Actually the wild bumblebees are preferable for young families. They sting mildly or not at all. One of my babies tried to eat one, but we wiped out his mouth and he did not seem to be harmed.

We should know more about birds than other wildlife since they so frequently appear in the press and on television. There are annual surveys of birds coming to gardens, and we are told that nearly 70 per cent of householders put out food in winter.

Certainly some birds have been driven away by the settlement. Only once, long ago did I hear a cuckoo – flying overhead and cuckooing in the early morning. Farm birds such as larks of course have gone. For years we had house sparrows settling in gardens for food, but now they too have waned. Starlings, which fly out in flocks from London roosts to forage for food in the suburbs, still come but in small numbers. Solitary birds, such as collared doves or magpies, still appear on our roofs, and the doves croon as if they were in a summer countryside. But our chief companions are blackbirds that still nest in a large copper-beech nearby, and in spring sing for sixteen hours a day. Thrushes have gone, but then they have gone from most places.

Redbury's most prominent bird is, as I suppose elsewhere, the black-headed gull in winter. The first sign of winter is a solitary gull standing, like a sentinel, on one of the small red roofs. Then hundreds arrive, white dotted on recreation ground and playing fields by day and black against the sunset as they fly to roost at sewage farms at night. They have always attracted attention. Unversed writers of historical fiction have put them on the Thames at the time of William the Conqueror, but actually they did not appear there, ornithologists say, till the hard winters at the end of the nineteenth century. I used to think our gull companies came from the Thames, but it seems that more likely they have come from the North in the winter migrations.

One frosty sunny morning I saw a dance that I had never seen before. About a dozen gulls were flying round the roofs, dipping and soaring in a circle. They swept round and round almost level with me at an upper window so that I could see the straining beaked faces which had a blank look as if all they thought of was the flight. They were dark against the pale blue sky and then white against the frosty ground, and they circled on and on for many minutes. There seemed no motive but pleasure in this wild rush of wings. Then suddenly the circle broke. There was a flurry, and then the skies were empty except for one last bird disappearing over a roof.

Since then in many winters I have seen this circling dance. It cannot be confined to Redbury, but I have never seen it described.

We have, of course, other wild visitors. Grey squirrels are not survivors from the fields but came in after the settlement was built. They are remarkable for the fierce emotions they create. Mr A., who has a large garden with many trees on the edge of Redbury, loathes them, calls them tree rats and shoots them. Miss B. with a large garden on the town side of Redbury loves them and feeds them on peanuts. Mrs C., with another large garden half a mile away, says that she is tired of them because the cat keeps on killing them. She has buried four and has no more room.

Within living memory there was a hunt over Redbury fields, and few people would want that restored. But feelings for foxes are mixed – surprise, dislike, admiration. Foxes have invaded along the railway lines bordered by small woods. They can be seen at night crossing roads, and once I saw a splendid large animal, killed presumably by traffic, laid out by a busy Thames-side road. One vixen lived for years in four big gardens behind a Victorian terrace and ate the grey squirrels and food put down by one resident. A neighbour told me that he often saw a fox stealing at midnight down a small side-road, and foxes were said to be breeding behind a near-by garage. One morning I found a huge hole excavated in my lawn and going under the hedge. Earth was scuffled in a wide circle, and it looked as if a tunnel had been tried and abandoned. On another night three plastic bags, one holding decayed vegetables, were left on my lawn.

But it was the hedgehog invasion that caused most stir some years ago.


Suddenly one spring people meeting in the shops were saying "Have you got one? What do you feed it on?"

Where had the hedgehogs come from? No-one knew, or knew if there was this surge all over the country. All we knew was that they were appearing in almost every garden. People were pleased to see them. They were part of our children's stories and never mind the fleas. Householders put out milk, bread and milk, bird-food and cat-food, and felt gratified when it had gone in the morning. The hedgehogs must have travelled, for flat spiny patches, the crushed animals, began to appear on our lethal road. The patches lasted for days.

We ourselves were lucky. The house next door had been empty for some months, and in spring the weeds grew up and the garden became a wilderness. Soon we were aware of small silent forms in the twilight, gliding under the hedge and across our yard. How many there were next door we did not know, but they overflowed into our garden. We too began to put out milk and were gratified if in the darkness the pale circle of the saucer was broken by the black triangle of a hedgehog snout. In the morning the saucer would be dry and marked by arrow-shaped dirty little footmarks.

The hedgehogs came in twilight and darkness, but we saw something of their behaviour. They never curled up in a ball as they were reputed to do but, if we approached, glided away under the hedge without a sound. They distinguished between ourselves and the cats. They took no notice when the cats approached, and the cats took no notice of them, both animals continuing their business as if the other did not exist.

At first the hedgehogs were silent, but later we became aware of small puffing noises round the garden. They sounded like little steam engines, and we concluded that these were mating sounds. Later still we caught glimpses of small processions round the paths – a large hedgehog in front and two or three tiny ones following.

Presently they were in our compost heap at the bottom of the garden. But summer passed all too quickly, and with August a wet season began. It rained for days, and we hoped that the compost heap was giving some protection. But one afternoon when I was at work the boys found two tiny flat hedgehog infants laid out side by side on the pile. They were less than two inches long, white, with buds where their spines would be, and they were moving feebly.

The human instinct is always to interfere. The boys carried the infants into the kitchen and tried to feed them with milk from a pipette. The infants refused it and made a mess; so the boys thought they might need warmth and put them on a sheet of newspaper and spread it in the airing cupboard.

I was told the story when I got home. I had never heard of hedgehogs in an airing cupboard, and it hardly seemed a suitable treatment. I also remembered the advice from naturalists when bird nestlings fall out of the nest, "Leave them alone and let the parents find them." The infant hedgehogs should go back to their proper home, I said. So the boys took them back to the compost heap and laid them side by side on top as before.

But my advice was disastrous. The infants had presumably been rejected by their kin anyhow, but when we went to look in the morning they were dead with great curved bites taken out of their flat little bodies. The kin had obviously not liked the smell of the boys or of the airing cupboard. The kind attentions of human beings are not wanted by wild creatures.

In the autumn the house next door was sold and the garden wilderness cleared up. We never knew what happened to the hedgehogs there or the hedgehogs in our compost heap or where all the rest went. They gradually vanished from the gardens, and there were no more spiny patches on the road. Only now and then did we hear of a lingering hedgehog. As with other wild creatures, their coming and going were a mystery.


It was some time after this when we were told that frogs would soon be extinct. It was as usual our fault. In Victorian times the frog had been regarded as the most convenient animal for dissection, and laboratories and schools cut them up in possibly millions. And now we were destroying their habitats, filling in the village ponds and damp ditches and substituting concrete.

It had all happened in a very short time. In our childhood garden near Redbury frogs were so common that they were hardly noticed. We did not eat them like the French, but they were part of daily life and stories and rhymes. They would hop about on a damp shady path overhung by a hazel tree and sometimes we would see a slow stout spotty toad.

But now an ecologist told me the story of a local school. It was taking part in a children's hour programme on television and needed a frog for demonstration. The children searched in vain in the half-built-up area round the school and then went to Richmond Park. There were no frogs there either. Finally they appealed to a school in Gloucestershire and a Midland frog was sent by train.

In Redbury the stream had been culverted and concrete was everywhere. Most gardens displayed neat annuals bought from garden centres and planted well apart with well-weeded ground between. What frog could survive?

But one afternoon a child knocked on my door to say that there was a rat in the garden shed. We were used to mice brought in by the cats, but rats were more formidable. I went to look and opened the shed door. Something moved at the back, but out came not a rat but a frog.

Where could it have come from and how had it got among the trowels and lawnmower? It loped to the door and scrambled out on to the flower-bed and slipped behind a clump of goldenrod. I tried to see where it would go, but it obliterated itself in the greenery and I lost it. I assumed that it would die, baked on the concrete or starved among clods of clay.

Some weeks later a child came up to tell me that there was a frog among the trees at the end of the garden. I went to look and was in time to see the splayed-out frog back quarters disappearing among scrub and roots. I put out a bowl of water and wondered what on earth the frog was doing down there. Then the children reported more frogs.

Later I met Mr F. who has a well-tended garden at the end of the alley. He told me he had made a double pool with a small waterfall between. The year before, one or two frogs had arrived, and this year the pools were teeming with frog life. There was so much spawn that, as a nature-lover, he had taken several buckets of it to country ponds up the road.

So that must be the explanation. All those old village ponds had been filled up, but now small suburban gardens were being given ponds of their own. Garden centres were advertising plastic sheeting to line a garden hole and water plants to go round it. All over the suburbs small sheets of water were appearing.

Later still one of the incessant wildlife surveys was announced by a frog expert at a Welsh university. He asked children all over the country to send in reports on frogs at their various stages of development. There had been a frog survey in 1988, but since then, it was thought, frogs had faded away. But thousands of reports came in, and they showed that frogs were still flourishing.

All the surveys with computers behind them make us feel as if we knew everything about wildlife. But there are still mysteries. I had found why frogs were in my garden, but how did the first frogs discover Mr F.'s pools, and where did they come from?

If you walk along our main road by daylight you see hardly a trace of wildlife. Cars speed endlessly and small red roofs spread in every direction. In the evening there may be gnats hovering over gates or a young bird pecking at dandelions or scraps of yarrow on the worn grass verge. There is little to lift the heart except perhaps the sky, vast over the low buildings. But all the time mysterious movements are going on in the small garden patches. We cannot be sure what they are because we can never see the world as foxes, hedgehogs or frogs see it.

# CHAPTER 11

# Children in Care. The Boy Who Did Not Come.

All this century there have been arguments about destitute children. In previous centuries they have been sent out as servants, half-starved in orphanages, sent overseas. At the beginning of the 1900s they were still being moved to Canada and Australia, but most of them were in barrack-like institutions, mostly run by charitable organisations.

At the beginning of the century many pious people regarded the begetting of children out of wedlock as a crime worse than murder – at any rate in the woman – and the shame spilled on to the children. But the children had to be maintained somehow and turned into good citizens. But how?

Fashions have swung to and fro – from large homes to small homes, to fostering and adoption and back again. Faults have appeared in all régimes, and even the long careful committee talks on individual children have been a disadvantage. For while the talks are going on the children are growing and, without parent figures, are being emotionally damaged. Even the practice of State support for unmarried mothers and their babies is being attacked, not only because it is expensive but because family patterns are repeated. Problem mothers produce more problem children, and flighty girls produce flighty daughters.

In the late mid-century when I came into contact with the system I was impressed at first by its kindness but later was burdened by its bureaucracy. Some things I did not understand at all.

I had seen something of large institutions in the 1930s and the deprivation of children without families. So when twenty years later I had some spare time at week-ends I rang up the nearest local-authority children's home and asked if any child needed a friend to take him out.

A cordial Scottish voice answered. The warden, Mr Douglas, said that he had only just come to the South to take charge of boys of five and over, and he did not know them well yet. Nearly all of them had some outside contact, but there was one newcomer of five who appeared to have no friends. Would I call?

It was past the time of huge institutions. Children were being lodged in small numbers, sent to ordinary schools and given as normal a life as possible. The house, I found, was among prosperous dwellings in an avenue leading to a church, and it had no sign of a council institution. I was shown into a small room with a well polished floor and comfortable gas-fire, and Mr Douglas, still young and without façade, came at once.

He told me the story of Graham who had just arrived. His mother, unmarried, had handed him to the authorities when he was just over one. She was now in Wales and sent him birthday and Christmas cards but took no further notice of him. Since his rejection he had been at the Council nursery down the hill. At the age of three he had had a good offer of adoption, but his mother would not consent. In those days the rights of natural parents were considered paramount; so the adoption offer was refused. It was the Council rule that when children reached the age of five they were moved to the "big boys' home", and Graham had been transferred. But he knew nobody, and, except for one visit, the nurses at his previous nursery had been too busy to come to see him. He might benefit from an outside friend.

"Would you like to see him?" Mr Douglas asked. I expected a low-looking child with a runny nose. Instead Graham was a little flower – pale, fair-haired, pretty with a large brow. I was not surprised that somebody had wanted to adopt him. He stood quietly and did not seem shy of a stranger as a child of his age might have been, but then he had no familiar figure to turn to. He said he would like to go out with me, and I said I would call the next Saturday afternoon.

So began our excursions. Graham was ready for me each Saturday afternoon. Our expeditions generally began with a "choosing", his word, at Woolworth's. We wandered round the store, and the girls smiled at his pale little face. He chose a present, and I generally bought him what he wanted, though I did demur at a bicycle. But his choice was mostly modest – a toy pistol or a xylophone – and

74

he obviously had no idea of the value of things. With his "choosing" he had an ice-cream.

Afterwards we went on some excursion, generally returning to my house to tea. Then I read him a story – he knew nothing about books – and got him back to the home by six.

Graham's unusual life had made him different from other children. He was accustomed to cars and buses but not to trains; so a walk above the railway line with trains running below was a treat. He knew something about church, for when we took him to a tea-room with panelled walls he said, "It's like church, isn't it?" He must also have had some scripture training, for when we stopped at a crafts shop, with some trifle with crossed pieces of wood in the window, he shouted to my embarrassment "Jesus on the cross. Bang .Bang. Bang."

His table manners were quite good, except that he seemed plagued with a fear of germs. If local children dropped a biscuit they would dust it and eat it, but Graham would hand it to me gravely saying, "There's germs on it, aren't there?"

Once I took him with a group of children to walk by the River Wey at Guildford. The others skipped about, but Graham walked soberly and seemed afraid of the stream. He kept on warning the others, "Keep away from the water. I'm telling yer. Keep away or yer'll be drownded." I could just hear the tones of an exasperated nurse from the home trying to control an outing.

He was afraid of many things – poison, germs, wasps, death. Once when it had been snowing and patches of white were on the path, he told me with an air of authority, "It'll kill yer if yer walk on it, won't it?" "It'll kill yer" was a frequent remark. We took him to a zoo, and he looked at the lions and tigers and commented, "They'll eat yer, won't they?" He did not seem to know many of the other animals, but he did recognise a parrot.

He was full of fantasies about his mother. Mum was going to give him a wrist watch. Mum often went up in an aeroplane. Mum had been to America. At first we believed his stories, but once we were on top of a bus and he looked down on a car ahead and said it was Mum's car and she was giving the Queen a ride. After that we were more sceptical.

We realised how much children talk of their families when, once or twice, Mr Douglas's son John came with us. He was a sturdy normal chatty boy a little younger than Graham but taller, and he dominated the conversation. His talk was all about "my mum" and "my dad", and there was Graham without a word to say. I realised that deserted children are not only deprived of families but of the chance to talk about them.

Quite early in our expeditions Graham began to ask to go " 'ome".

" 'Ome" was the nursery down the hill where he had lived before he had been plucked out and sent to the home for older boys. I was quite willing to take him, but Mr Douglas said that Graham's future was being discussed, and "we'd better go carefully at present." So I never took him, and as the months passed he did seem to forget the nursery though who knew what inner stresses remained?

Meanwhile Mr Douglas was trying to get to know him, and told met that the boy might be musical. "I notice, when we put on the television, it's the tunes he listens to more than looking at the pictures." I should have liked to find if he had musical talent, but was not given the time.

Graham always gathered a pile of oddments to take home with him as well as his "choosing". Wrapping paper, string, scraps from crackers, old envelopes were all collected and screwed into a parcel. I thought at first the he was starved of possessions, but each boy had a locker in a line and later I saw some of the other boys' collections in the lockers. All seemed bursting with the same kind of rubbish, and I assumed it was a reaction to being in a home where few things are really yours.

For a time when Graham grew used to our excursions he became very obstreperous. He would march sharply out of the home gate and down the road, but when we reached a curve and the home was hidden he would fall into a furious temper, frowning, kicking, stopping dead and refusing to hold my hand. I would grow angry too; ask him if he wanted to go back and finally turn about towards the home again. That brought him to his senses, and he became docile and by the end of the afternoon was affectionate and cheerful, eating a large tea and afterwards sitting on my knee for a read. He seemed to know nothing about books, but he enjoyed Beatrix Potter and other children's favourites. I was careful to follow the home's rules and deliver him back – with a slight feeling of relief – by six.

When autumn came I asked Mr Douglas if Graham would want to continue the outings. He said emphatically that Graham looked forward all the week to Saturdays and weather would make no difference. So we continued the excursions, spending longer in my house. Once I had a bad cold and was afraid of spreading infection, but Mr Douglas did not want Graham to be disappointed. So I got someone else to take him out.

As time went on Graham said less about things "killing yer", and seemed to be developing into a normal little boy.

But Christmas was a disaster. We invited Graham for Christmas Day, but Mr Douglas said he must remain at the home, as the mayor was paying it a visit. Indeed, when I saw the preparations I realised that we could never equal them. Local authorities always make much of Christmas at children's and old people's homes as if they were trying to compensate for the inmates' misfortune in being there. Graham's home had a large Christmas tree, festoons of bells, sparkling artificial frost and tinsel, cotton-wool snow, balloons and coloured lights. Nothing we could do would equal Mr Douglas's effort.

"Have him on Boxing Day," Mr Douglas said.

It was bitter cold that day. Graham was even paler than usual and said little. I took him straight back to our house and gave him presents, but he did not seem to enjoy them and ate little tea. Then he began to say monotonously, "Want to go 'ome. Want to go 'ome," "'ome" now being his present residence. Then he trailed up to the lavatory and was very sick on the stairs.

I wrapped him in a blanket in front of the fire, but he continued to ask for " 'ome"; so I took him back. I had no car, and the bus was a long time coming, and there was a bitter wind. Ordinary boys would probably have complained, but Graham waited stoically while I worried. The bus came at last, and finally I delivered him to the warmth and brightness of the home. He revived a little, and Mr Douglas said he would put him straight to bed.

Graham was a tough little boy in spite of his pallor. He was well enough and anxious to go out on the following Saturday and our jaunts continued till the spring. Gradually the evenings grew light again, and it was daylight when I took him back at six o'clock. By this time our own house had become " 'ome".

On our way back from the bus-stop we passed a retired countrified road shaded by tall trees. In my childhood it had been a mysterious way into the country, but I had not been there lately, and more houses had been built, but to me it still kept an air of another world. So when Graham asked, "Who lives there?" I said without thinking that it might be fairies. I was surprised at the way he latched on to this. Somebody must have mentioned fairies to him, but he had had no-one to tell him stories. After that, every time we passed the road, he asked what the fairies were doing.

He was now at school and beginning to realise that there was a world outside his " 'ome". On those spring evenings our return along his avenue was held up by his enquiries. He would stop outside each gate and ask, "Who lives here?"

I made up stories till I grew tired.

"Who lives here?"

"Mrs Biggles."

"What's she doing?"

"Putting her children to bed."

"And who lives here?"

"Mr Watson."

"And what's *he* doing?"

In the end I would grow afraid that we should be late back and had to stop the game.

One summer Saturday we got permission to take Graham for a day to friends at Worthing. On that day he was a boy to be proud of. He was neatly dressed and pretty, spoke quite well and ate enormously. At the end of the visit, though he was tired, he did not complain, but quietly fell asleep in the bus.

And, though Mr Douglas was an admirable warden and the home was comfortable, we said, "It's a shame we have to take him back."

But by this time it seemed that Graham might live permanently with us. I was willing to foster him, and an official from the children's department called. He suggested that I should take the boy out every Sunday as well as Saturday to prepare him for the change. Then, he said, it was likely that Graham would come to us.

For several months I devoted almost the whole of the week-end to

Graham – and then it all came to nothing.

I never knew why. Several officials were concerned, and they seemed not to know what one another was doing. Mr Douglas repeatedly said that he was only an employee and had no power.

One week-end Graham announced that he had two friends now – me and another lady. He seemed pleased at this. Mr Douglas confirmed that a Mrs Rock had been invited to foster Graham. She had a boy of seven and wanted a companion for him. It was a surprise, but I did not protest. Mrs Rock had the boy of seven, which I had not, and she did not to go out to work and I did.

I wondered if the official who had called had taken some dislike to us. But it seemed that the official who had made the arrangements with Mrs Rock had not known at all that we had been taking Graham out.

Now the Children's Department worked quickly. When I telephoned as usual on the Thursday I was told that Graham was leaving that week-end. I had no chance to say goodbye.

One tends to think of children's departments as wise, and it was not for me to criticise, but I had been shocked at the way Graham had been moved suddenly from his babies' home and all contact cut off. Now, it seemed, it was happening again. And why did the department choose Mrs Rock?

Some weeks later I asked Mr Douglas for Graham's new address. Christmas was coming and I wanted to send Graham a present.

Mr Douglas gave me the address. "But I don't think you'll get much from it," he said firmly. He had invited Mrs Rock to bring Graham back to the home to see the boys, but she had absolutely refused. She said she was going to make a clean break.

So it had happened a third time – in babyhood, at five and now. And in those days at least foster mothers could apparently do as they pleased.

One of Graham's favourite books had been *Little Black Mingo* , the story of the little Indian girl and the crocodile. I tried to buy a copy, but it was out of print and unobtainable. So I spent some hours cleaning up and re-lettering our old copy. I sent it to Graham at Christmas with a note to Mrs Rock inviting her to come to tea with her boy and Graham.

But Mr Douglas had been right. I never had an answer.

In a bus some time later I met one of the nurses from Graham's old nursery.

I asked how Graham was getting on. She said she knew little as she had moved to a new district, but she had heard that his conduct was not very good.

I was not surprised.

But I never heard any more of Graham.

# CHAPTER 12
## *Per Ardua. The Lone Woman*

Probably in no other century have women had to struggle so much on their own. The triumphant Suffragette movement brought freedom in one way. On the other hand the two World Wars with their slaughter deprived thousands of women of partners. The husbands and fiancés had gone, and girls who had hardly heard of women's rights, and would not have bothered about them anyhow, were left unprotected, often to play the part of men.

Mrs Annie May, whom we met in her later years, had no children, and her status as a married woman was obscure, but she was in some ways a good example of a struggler. But what she wanted and worked for was not a family or male support but simply a "little home".

She was one of the housekeepers who came after the second war to look after my two boys while I worked in London. But she was different from the rest, sacking herself sometimes and then coming back, staying on and off till her death. She ended by getting her "little home" together and inhabiting it for some years, but she was beaten in the end by old age and blindness. However, she must have had a good long innings, working till she was nearly eighty.

Yet one could not have guessed her age when she called on that summer evening. I had notified a domestic agency that I needed a housekeeper, and it sent along Mrs Annie May whom we always knew as "Nanna". She must have been at least sixty, but she had dyed her hair with a reddish tinge and she wore it in a pony-tail. She had a smart white dress, a green sweater and high-heeled white shoes. She told us that she had been offered a maisonette in a local estate being built by a charitable trust. "I want a job out here, see," she said. She wore large glasses but did not mention deficient eyesight. "I've got a pension; so I won't charge you much," she urged.

She gave the impression of being absolutely intent on getting the job, and she got it. Yes, she could cook. Yes, she would be punctual every morning. Yes, she knew how to manage children. She whirled us into an agreement in a quarter of an hour. She was not perhaps a person to stir deep emotions, but she was hardy and amusing and she was to entertain us through many years. By degrees I learnt some, though not all, of her history.

Mrs Annie May was very fond of animals – in two ways. She loved dogs and cats, but she also had an idyllic memory of Sunday suppers of her youth when the sideboard groaned under lots of cold meats.

Her father was in the wine trade, and home was near Hammersmith Bridge. She had three brothers, and as they grew up they brought in their friends. Nanna would have had a good time, but it was a little spoiled by her bad eyesight. She had had measles in her childhood, and the doctor said she would have to wear glasses her whole life. All the same it was fun with all those young men.

While she was still in her teens the Great War broke out. The young men rushed to enlist, and the girls rushed to marry them. So Nanna got married too – to Jack, a friend of her brothers. The couple had a fortnight together at the seaside, and then Jack went to France and was killed. "I didn't mind much," Nanna told me. "I never liked him much."

There were gaps in her story, but she emerged having a good time with Harry after the war. Ah – but she did love Harry. He, like her father, was in the wine trade and he had plenty of money. They had fun at the races and then they went to Paris and did a round of the music halls. Nanna enjoyed the "dirty bits".

At some time in her early thirties she had "all her inside out" so that she could not have children. She alluded to this casually and did not explain the cause. But it did not matter. She did not want children and she had Harry and a nice home. But then Harry got a bad cough, and the doctor said that he had a weak chest and must spend the winter in a warm climate. So he went to South Africa, and then Nanna had a note that he was dead.

This seemed strange, but an explanation may have been given by an unpleasant brother after Nanna's death. He said she was not Mrs Annie May at all and had never been married to Harry. But it did not matter to her by that time.

But it must have mattered after Harry's death, for Nanna lost her "little home". Gradually the property had to be sold and she had to support herself. From then on her goal in life was to get together a home again.

She next emerged at an aircraft factory in the last war. By then she was a small middle-aged woman who stood up for her rights and enjoyed the good things of life. She put on trousers through they were only just becoming acceptable for women, and this and her penchant for dirty stories earned her the nickname of "Bobby". She always, she told us, arrived early for work, and indeed punctuality was one of her virtues. But she always downed tools early too.

She was collecting property for her "little home", and when there was nothing in the shops she bought from acquaintances or looked in the papers for advertisements. It was typical that, a few weeks after she had joined us, when an American friend called on me, Nanna approached her boldly and asked if she had any nylon stockings to sell. At the time nylons were available in the United States but not in England. "A very vulgar person," the friend said, and Nanna did not get her nylons. But life had made her aggressive, and aggression often worked.

It worked at the end of the war. Nanna had had another stroke of bad luck. She had been lodging with an old lady, but the old lady died and the house was to be sold. So Nanna, with the war job at an end, had nowhere to go. At the time there was the frantic housing shortage, and all the emphasis was on finding homes for people with families.

But Nanna kept bothering the housing authorities, and she bothered so hard that she was finally lodged in a large house set aside for those made homeless by air raids. She was the only single woman there, and she hated it. We heard stories of it afterwards. It was a decayed house with a dilapidated garden since nobody took the trouble to look after it. The wives had not enough to do and gossiped and ganged up against Nanna, and there was a large monkey-faced man whom she called Tarzan. He made a nuisance of himself because he had a lady-like wife and he felt inferior. He never said good morning, and he came in late and banged doors and woke Nanna up. In the summer he sunned himself, naked to the waist, in the garden, in sight of all the windows. "Disgusting I call it," Nanna said. We were to learn that "disgusting" was one of her favourite words.

It was a purposeless life anyhow, and Nanna wanted a job. She went back to the housing department and made another fuss. There she heard that a charitable trust four miles away was building an estate of maisonettes for elderly people. She did not know the district, but, seeking a "little home", she applied. She got her maisonette, went to a domestic agency and heard we had a job near the new estate, and came straight to us. She was determined to join us, and I was relieved not to have to do more searching. So, at her own request, she began to work with us in a few days.


Nanna always arrived punctually though at the beginning her road was only half made. But she generally enjoyed a good grumble when she appeared. "Shocking" was another favourite word. "Shocking hot day," she would say on a warm June morning, or "shockingly windy" in a September breeze. "Did you read of that shocking murder?" she would say with relish, and would add, "Brussels sprouts are a shocking price."

But the fine things beginning to appear in the shops after the war helped to atone for the world's shockingness. She recommended many household goods to me – tinned rice, plastic cushions, detergents, ready-made pastry – and she had a keen eye for bargains. She heartily disapproved of my shopping.

"Now where did you get that cabbage? Look, it's going quite yellow. I get *my* cabbage straight from the ground – from the nursery across the road... Now where did you get those strawberries? Quite squashy underneath, some of them. Yesterday I got *my* strawberries from a man at the door. Every berry firm."

In spite of poor sight she regularly studied the local papers for bargains for her "little home". She bought an electric cooker for two pounds but later decided that she preferred gas and bought a gas-stove on hire purchase. She had one small carpet, but a neighbour hired a vacuum cleaner and, not to be outdone, Nanna did the same.

One or twice she invited us to tea at her little home. I could not help being impressed. One turned from a windy main road into a sheltered paved path beside low brick buildings, each composed of two maisonettes, each with its front door. Small gardens were in front, and ancient country trees had been left for amenity. When we arrived and went up the stairs we found a bright fire, a large oak tree outside the window and a general impression of orange draperies. At our first visit one of the boys said tactlessly "Why, that's ours," noting an orange chair-back. Nanna had been dipping into our rag drawer and found the discarded bit of material. It just suited her colour scheme. When I congratulated her on the general comfort she remarked complacently, "I must be artistic or something."

Someone on the estate went to a chiropodist; so Nanna went to him as well though what he did to her feet we never heard. One summer she noticed that many people were going to Scotland; so Nanna decided she would go as well. It rained most of the time and I expected a harvest of "shockings" when she returned; but she was as pleased as punch. "I met ever such a nice person, a retired lady, and we did everything together. Took trips in all those buses. Have you been to Scotland and seen the buses? And splendid food we had. Those teas they give you! I"m getting quite a belly on me."

Nanna had gifts that we did not expect. She was an excellent cook, and made delicious coffee, though she slopped it over on the saucer because of her poor sight. When she took the boys to the playground she went, in her trousers, down the slide with them. She surprised us one Christmas, when the boys were given a xylophone. We hammered at it tentatively, but Nanna seized it and banged out a nearly perfect "Good King Wensceslas". She had songs too, some of them ribald, but including the one about the "doggy in the window".

Used to the hard knocks of the world, she had little reverence for authority and was to quarrel with the local vicar over a cat. She took one of my boys on a walk past the parish church and found the door open and pushed in. He told me that she had gone up into the pulpit and preached a sermon. I asked him what she had said, but apparently it was not much. She had declared that God and the Devil were in the world, apparently of equal status, doing secret deeds, and presumably one should be on God's side.

Through the years we heard a good deal about Nanna's estate. The old people seemed to get on fairly well together, but she regarded most of them with detachment. "We've been having such goings-on. The old man under me has put his head in a gas-oven. His wife died six months ago, and he didn't like living on his own. I'm glad it wasn't me who found him."

Or in winter, "Three deaths in one week. Well, we do see life."

She was jealous of her rights and objected to the boys who came and kicked a football round a side field that belonged to the estate. "I warned them lads, great foul-mouthed brutes, but they wouldn't go away. So I rang up Scotland Yard..."

"You mean the local Police," I said. But no. She had tackled London headquarters. And the call worked. "In half an hour along comes a bobby, and in a second them and their damn ball had gone."

Nanna made one friend on the estate. This was Gladys, a retired Civil Servant, of higher education than the others though she seemed to be a friend to all of them. She occupied a comfortable ground-floor flat with armchairs, flowers and, wonder of wonders, a shelf of books. But Gladys was sick with cancer and not expected to live long.

Nanna got to know her through their dogs. Gladys had an intelligent terrier, and Nanna presently purchased "Sally" – the abominable mongrel that was to become her life. When Gladys was still strong enough to walk, the two exercised their dogs together, and Nanna often went to relax in Gladys's comfortable sitting-room. She shocked me a little later when it was known that Gladys's cancer was incurable. She boarded the housing authorities again and asked if she could have Gladys's maisonette when she died. The desire to better her "little home" was still predominant. But, as it happened, Nanna died a few months before Gladys.


It was the usual story with Nanna. Other people on the estate had dogs; so she must have one too. She paid two guineas, a large sum in those days, for an odd-looking puppy. "I bought her for a poodle," she said later. "But she's turning out not quite a pedigree."

Sally grew and grew and became a great ill-tempered shambling creature, pulling Nanna along with her chain and shedding white hairs everywhere. Yet Nanna loved her "little dog". Once I met a friend of hers in the bus, and remarked that I had been to see Mrs Annie May.

"To tell you the truth," the friend said, "me and Annie have had words. It was that pest of a dog. She comes down with it, and it leaves its hairs all over the house. 'I got a new carpet, Annie,' I says. 'For Pete's sake leave that dog at home.' But no. Down she comes trotting with that Sally. 'I can't have her in no more,' I says. 'I have to go all over the house with a brush and dustpan after your Sally's been about.' 'Oh,' she says. 'If it's like that I'd better go home,' and she turns and never comes in. And I wasn't sorry, I can tell you, with that great dog scattering its coat all over the place. 'Tain't healthy. She hasn't been since."

They had been friends for years and had visited each other weekly, but the dog won. Sally, though Nanna was always pulling at her chain and asking, "Where's that stick?" had become an inseparable companion. She was always, "that faithful little dog".

Once or twice in the gaps in her work for us Nanna appeared with Sally on a Sunday afternoon. Nanna was smart on these occasions with red-tinted hair piled high and a lemon-coloured sweater. But nothing could make Sally look smart. Hairs would fly about, and Nanna would excuse this by saying that the dog had skin trouble. She had been to the vet and got some stuff for the bare patches, but it did not seem to have worked.

We would bring out biscuits, which Sally would lick up in a twinkling, Nanna shouting at her all the time to "lie down. Where's that stick?" We too had to go over our carpets when they left.

Once Nanna paid ten and sixpence, a considerable sum for her, to have Sally trimmed as a poodle. The effect was bizarre, and Nanna did not repeat the experiment. Anyhow by that time her income was stretched. She had had a quarrel with the vicar, and there was another mouth to feed.

The parish church stood high on the hill near Nanna's estate, and she noticed a stray black cat in the churchyard. Being fond of animals she began to feed it each day, and once she met the vicar among the graves. She told us that she had urged him to find a home for the cat. "He wasn't interested," she reported. "So I told him he was no Christian."

In the end she took the cat to her maisonette, and Sally did not seem to mind. But the the problem of expense arose. She had not the money for both dog and cat. "You take the cat," she said to me. We already had one black cat, but we could not turn Nanna's protégé away. So she brought him down – a rusty sour animal with a strident honking voice. We called him Foghorn.

Immediately there was trouble. Foghorn did not care for us at all, and he and our own cat developed an undying hatred. For months we tried to keep the peace, feeding them in separate rooms and letting one out to sit at the front and the other to sit at the back. But then autumn came, and they had to be more together. And then Foghorn disappeared.

We searched round the alleys but discovered nothing. I found, as I had found before, that one is helpless when a cat runs away. However, we did put a "lost" note on our gate, and this brought a woman knocking at our door. She said that there was a cat like Foghorn haunting the gardens in a side road which we had not searched because it had a flow of traffic and seemed too busy for a refuge. But the woman brought the cat along, and it was Foghorn all right. He had reverted to scrounging, apparently preferring hunger to our company.

We welcomed him back and took him to the vet to have his teeth cleaned. The vet said that he was probably very old but hardy. As the cold weather began the two cats seemed to be bearing one another a little better, and one evening we thought that peace might come. It was very foggy, and our cat came in as Foghorn asked to go out. Passing one another by the door the two touched noses, and it seemed a gesture of friendship. Instead it was gesture of farewell.

Foghorn went out into the night and never came back. Again we wandered up and down looking for him and put a notice on the gate. But this time there was no response.

We had to tell Nanna, and she was upset and adopted her censorious tone. "Well, he didn't run away from *me*." Foghorn must have been killed, she said, trying to cross the road to get back to her. But I did not think so. Neighbours near by always reported such accidents, and we had heard nothing. Foghorn had probably gone some way away and returned to scrounging.

We felt guilty, but at least Nanna still had Sally.

Then Nanna fell ill.

It was in the heart of the winter with dirty snow and grey skies. Her friend Gladys rang up after a week-end to say that Mrs Annie May had a bad cold and the doctor said it looked life influenza.

The week passed, and we heard no more. Neither Nanna nor Gladys had a telephone; so we could not ring up. I was working and could not go out till the Saturday, but in the afternoon I walked up to the estate. The wind was bitterly cold along the approach road, now edged with small houses, and snowflakes drifted down. Nanna, I thought, might be awkward at times, but she was admirably punctual in spite of the daily struggle down the exposed road.

I went along the side path of the estate. All the doors were shut, and nobody was about, but Nanna's door opened as I turned the handle. I heard a scuffle, and there was the great hairy Sally on the stairs. She barked as usual, but nobody took any notice.

Nanna was in bed, lying on her side with her knees drawn up. Her face was flushed and her eyes closed. She looked different, gentle and more defenceless, without her glasses. I did not wake her. There were pill bottles by the bed, and she was obviously being looked after. I left her and went round knocking on doors to find who was in charge, but on that Saturday afternoon everybody seemed to be out. In the end I went home.

It was no good writing letters. Her bad sight prevented her from reading them. The only contact was through visits. I heard nothing during the next week but went back on the Saturday. But this time her door was locked, and there was no Sally to bark. It could not be that... I went round knocking on doors again.

A woman looked out of a window and told me to go to Mrs Robinson. "*She* knows. I keep meself to meself."

Mrs Robinson, however, was fat and friendly. "She's been moved away. She couldn't look after herself. The doctor said take his pills every three hours, but how was she to tell the time? The ambulance come for her yesterday." She named a local hospital. "She was very ill. I don't know I'm sure. The doctor said send for her brother in London. Not that he's any good to her. It's hard when you're old..."

So the familiar Nanna, on her way to the Valley of the Shadow, became mysterious. I thought over her life and was glad that it had finished with a "little home" and that she had had a companion in the abominable Sally.

Later I screwed up my courage and rang the hospital.

The operator who answered said that she had not heard anything about the death of a Mrs Annie May, but she would put me through to the ward. The ward did not seem to have heard anything about a death either. A nurse said, "I'll fetch sister."

The sister sounded cheerful. "Well, I'm sorry. She won't be able to come to you for a few weeks."

"A few *weeks*? You mean she's getting better?"

"Oh, it'll take a month or so, you know."

So there was nothing to mourn over after all. Nanna became herself again.


She was thinner but certainly her human self when she came out of hospital. She had always enjoyed a cigarette, as almost everybody else did in those days, but she said she had given up smoking. The self-denial did not last long, however. Meanwhile she had become famous.

"That faithful little dog, my dear – Gladys fed her and was good to her. But Sally sat at the window watching for me for five weeks. She just waited and waited... You should have seen the fuss, my dear when I came home. I might have been Royalty. And the flowers. And the presents. People brought me plates of dinner. They went shopping for me...

"I like the Red Cross. Someone told them about me, and now they're bringing dinner four days a week. And they come in a car to take me to their social centre. There are a lot of poor old dears down there. They make me laugh."

But this state of euphoria did not last. Nanna soon discovered that she did not relish the company of the old dears and sacked herself from the centre. She also sacked a home help sent by the Council.

"It was awkward with that woman. There wasn't room for both of us in the maisonette. While she was cleaning I used to go and sit on a bench outside. But it was cold there; so I told her I didn't want her no more."

Then Nanna decided that she would like another job. "I should be blessed bored sitting here all day." We had had to bring in another help; so Nanna considered other prospects though she must have been over seventy. She was willing to take on anything. My elder boy was pea-licking in the school holidays. So Nanna thought she might go pea-picking too. She heard that the Council cooked school meals, and she thought she might join the cooks. Then she saw a factory advertisement in a local paper.

She went down to the factory and found an old man at the gate. "Only young girls wanted here," he said.

Nanna was indignant. "You're no chicken yourself," she retorted. "Damn cheek," she said to me.

Finally she got a job as a night attendant to a senile old lady in a wealthy house. But she still visited us and regaled us with Rabelaisian details. The old lady was a great bother, and her wits had gone. But she had a much younger "lovely" gentlemen for a husband. Nanna had an eye for men, and she liked talking to him. He was very kind to the old lady and polite to Nanna, and paid her wages regularly. Later her enthusiasm waned. He had ceased to talk to her much, and the old lady's antics were growing worse. But Nanna stuck to the job, making it as easy as possible. She took down a blanket and got a good many hours of sleep on a sofa in the old lady's bedroom. She was not sure if she should be doing this, and did not mention it to the gentleman.

She was very merry over the old lady. "She gets up in the middle of the night, my dear. Wants to dress and go out. The other night she took hold of a basket and said she was going shopping. She was too much for me; so I got the gentleman, and he calmed her down. I wonder he doesn't get fed up."

Nanna stayed in the job for more than a year, but then the old lady grew ill and a day nurse was called in. One evening Nanna arrived at the house and was told that the old lady had died. The gentleman paid her wages and give her an extra five pounts, and said she need not come back.

Nanna did not grieve at all over the old lady and did not go to the funeral. But she did grieve some months later when she saw in the local paper that the lady had left sixty-five thousand pounds. "She might have left me a little," she grumbled. "I could have done with a thousand pounds, and she wouldn't have missed it. I could just have done with a thousand."

And now her sight had become too bad for another job. She went up to the eye hospital every six months, but it kept her waiting, saw her only for five minutes and told her to come back in another six months.

I realised how bad her sight was when I saw her down at the shops. Sally seemed to be acting as guide dog and pulling her along, and Nanna looked vacant and – at last – old. She did not see me.

Her "little home" was deteriorating as she could not see to clean properly, and she began to do what she had mocked in the old lady – turn night into day. There were complaints that she was going round the estate and knocking on people's doors at midnight. Even Gladys was perturbed. "I heard a loud knocking on my door at two o'clock in the morning and there was Mrs Annie May with Sally. I had to tell her to go home."

I had long been trying to persuade Nanna to let me talk to her doctor, who seemed to be neglecting her. She agreed at last, and I telephoned to complain. But I found that he was the one who was complaining. He said that for months he had been trying to persuade her to give up her maisonette and go into a home. "She can't continue like this. She is nearly blind." I said I would talk to her.

So after all that striving for the "little home" it would have to be given up. The doctor found it difficult to hear of a place for an old blind woman, but at last she was offered accommodation in a London home. But he said that he did not think the home would take Sally.

Nanna was to move in ten days, but then she did not have to move after all – at least not to the London institution. She developed a cold and then pneumonia, and this time the hospital reports were not reassuring. She died in a few days.

Gladys and I were left to clear up. Sally had been lodged with a vet, who rang me up and asked what he was to do with the dog. "I can't keep her. She's very aggressive and is attacking the other dogs."

I was reluctant, but what could one say? So Sally had to go to join her mistress. Then the Council asked us to clear Nanna's maisonette as it was needed for another tenant. The task fell mainly on Gladys, though she was ill, as I was working in the week. But on a Saturday I went to help and meet Nanna's brother who had come down with his wife from London to see what he could pick up.

He was a small rat-faced man, and I understood why he had never helped Nanna. It was then that he said with a sneer that Mrs Annie May had no right to call herself by the name. She was really – but I did not catch the name he gave her.

We took the couple to the maisonette, and they said they would look for anything they wanted. We left them to the task and Gladys made tea for them. They came at last and said they had found money in all sorts of places, including the fridge. They had gathered twenty pounds altogether, but they did not offer any to Gladys. Nor did they thank her for the tea.

When she returned to the maisonette she found it in utter confusion, furniture moved and drawers pulled out. It was cold weather and there was no heat in the rooms, and she was ill, but she tidied up and managed to sell some of the furniture to neighbouts. The money just covered Nanna's debts. Gladys herself died a few months later, but by that time Nanna's affairs had been cleared. She had still been buying an expensive gas-stove on the hire-purchase system.

# CHAPTER 13

# Neighbours. The Good Woman.

This century has probably brought more quarrels between neighbours than ever before. People, often fairly affluent and cocksure, have been settled in housing estates with small gardens divided only by low palings or hedges. The houses have been small, which has meant a good deal of living outside, and the activities of one family have provoked another. "The best neighbour", one woman said to me, "is the one you don't know is there."

Some annoyances, such as bonfires and noise at night, have recently been controlled though they were not regulated in the mid-century. Others, such as branches overhanging fences, children's playthings thrown over fences, barking dogs, shouting radios and barbecues making stifling paraffin smells, remain. And some injuries are intentional. I once found an old woman sitting on a roadside bench and crying. "It's them next door," she said. "A family of five with three young devils. One's already been in prison, and they're all out of work. I live alone with no-one to protect me. They jump over my fence, kick about the garden and hammer the door. Their latest trick is laying down in front of my gate so as I can't get in or out."

"Neighbours are more important than relations," one elderly man said. But there is another side. All over the estates neighbours are helping each other – looking after children and pets, visiting the lonely, taking in parcels. Some do good deeds in a wide circle. Babs Wright was one of them. She made only one unkind judgment, and she gave that up in the end.

Babs must have been in her early fifties when I first knew her. She had thin brown neatly waved hair, a trim figure and neat ankles. Her clothes were quiet in colour but fairly expensive. But the chief impression was of gold-rimmed spectacles beaming good will on the world.

She was unusual in being one of a foursome – two couples living closely together with a back-garden gate linking their properties. They had moved to Redbury together. In the 1920s she and her little cherry-cheeked husband Frank were living in a picturesque village, now suburbanised. Next door to them were the Greens – Tom and Annie, a quiet couple only a little older. It was the infertile era before the war when fewer children than usual were being born and pundits were lamenting a dying nation. Neither Wrights nor Greens had children, and, instead, they became close friends. Babs may possibly have been the chief influence. She loved the pale Annie Green next door.

One summer Sunday the four walked along lanes to see the developments rumoured at Redbury. Building was still in its early stages, but a house-agent's office showed new houses for sale. A thunderstorm came on, and the four sheltered in the house agent's doorway and looked at the photographs in the window. Both couples were fairly secure financially. Babs's family had a small factory, and her husband Frank worked there. Tom was employed by a local Council. So, sheltering from the storm, they asked one another, "Why don't we...?"

They took two houses together on the main road, which then was narrow and fairly quiet. The houses were at the end of a terrace of four and were called condescendingly "workmen's dwellings". Roughcast with red-tiled roofs they were small, with short front gardens and long narrow back gardens, sloping down towards a dip with a stream. On the rise opposite were fields. I think the house price was £400 each.

The houses suited them. Annie Green several times commented to me later on the solidity of the materials, better than the trashy stuff used after the war. It was the surroundings that were to dismay them.

Building was proceeding all over the place, and to protect themselves the couples planted trees back and front. Tom Green set a privet hedge along his front and back borders with the farther property, and the hedge flourished and grew high and thick. It was over this that I used to talk to him when we arrived years later.

The war came. The two men were too elderly to be called up or were in reserved occupations. Babs worked happily at a nearby headquarters of NAAFI, the Forces' catering organisation. I never heard what Annie did, but she was probably not strong enough to do much. A few bombs dropped but not enough to disturb the settlement.

After the war building began again on a vast scale. The fields behind the main-road houses were covered with more small roads and small red-roofed buildings. Shops were built in a double line, and the main road in between was thronged with more and more traffic. Crowds of people came out from towns. Babs, generally so pleased with her fellows, surprised me once by saying, "Redbury is a very vulgar place."

The two couples discussed moving again, but they had been settled for years, and the area was convenient for the men's jobs. So they planted their gardens, and shielded themselves as best they could. Tom had made a terrace garden, and the Wrights had grass and many trees. I used to think when I stood there, sheltered from the road traffic by the higher line of houses, that it was almost like being in the country.

The two families had different social habits. Tom, the square-headed, bald countryman, and Annie, his delicate wife, had few visitors. Babs, on the other hand, knew people all over the place and constantly entertained. Her shopping jaunts were punctuated by long conversations when she stood on the pavement with her bag beside her, and she would stand at her front gate and chat to passers-by. She visited old people – taking bottles of Bovril. "I have great faith in Bovril," she said. And in family disasters she would appear sympathetically at the door with a bottle of brandy.

I remember one dramatic incident from her later days. Old Mr Batt, who lived at the end of the row – well-known for his fuchsias and his stocky form at the gate watching the traffic – had died and left a widow and her sister in the house. Babs began to take the two old ladies shopping each week as both were over seventy. One day they had shopped and returned with their bags, and the sister went upstairs to take her coat off. She did not come down, and when they went to look for her she was found dead on the bed. Such are the ripples that stir a close community, and Babs told the story many times. The remaining sister finally went into a home.

The Wrights had a small car, with Frank, the cherry-cheeked husband, doing the driving. He was an amiable, shy little man who would go and put the car away while Babs gossiped with somebody they had met, and he acted as an excellent foil to her vivacity. They took other people, including the Greens, for drives and visited Babs's well-off family in an affluent district beyond Leatherhead.

Every summer the Wrights spent a fortnight at Swanage, going to the same place each year because Babs had made good friends with the landlady. Once I met them at Waterloo Station when they were returning and I was coming back from work. As we travelled to our home station Babs discoursed in her pleased way on the holiday. Then she insisted on my sharing a taxi to Redbury and would not let me pay.

The Wrights frequently went back to their old village to see friends and the bank. Babs would not change the bank and said the manager was like a father to her. She was to go to him for advice later.

After years the comparatively tranquil life was shattered. Annie, who had had operations for cancer, was ill again. Babs, who, with all her other activities, had gone through the garden gate to visit her each morning, was the support of the troubled households. Annie's was a slow decline, with visits to hospital and returns home, and I saw something of it as in those days neither household had a telephone and I took messages for them. Once or twice when I went to Tom's house with some message Babs opened the door and seemed to be cooking supper for him.

Annie returned to hospital finally, and one evening I had a message, "Come at once." She died that night with the three of them there.

A few days later I had a shock. Babs was talking about Annie, and suddenly she became angry and began a bitter attack on Tom. I had never seen the slightest sign of dissension between the couples before, but now Babs said that Tom was a dolt, a fool, quite incapable of business. "Frank and I had to make all the arrangements for the funeral and do all the other business. All through Annie's illness we've had to look after things. He'd have been in a poor way without us."

Later she abused Tom again. She told me that Annie had once said to her, "What sort of life have I had?" She had had no life because of Tom, Babs said. He had been an idiot husband, and Annie had had years of unhappiness.

I knew this was not entirely true. Tom had told me that marriage had been the first happiness of his life, and "Me and my missus never have a rough word." The pale stooping Annie, whom my boys called "Mrs Mouse", had often gone twice down to the shops in a day for provisions for Tom and said, "Tom always likes his bread fresh." She had also shown off with pride a large model sailing ship that Tom had made. She kept it on the back-room table.

Meanwhile Tom in his wooden way mourned in secret. He continued at the old house and garden jobs saying little, and now himself went down to the shops in his long old-fashioned coat and cap or trilby which made him look different from the modern hatless generation. Then he began a time-killer with the buses. He had given up his long cycle rides, but had a free bus pass and went on solitary expeditions. Not to the country, as I at first thought, but to look at building in other suburbs. It was a time when many towns were creating pedestrian precincts and new block-like public buildings, and Tom, as a former Council employee, was interested. He would have a meal out and return late in the afternoon with most of the lonely day over. I never now heard any communication between the two houses.

But before long Babs had other things to think of. Now the self-effacing little Frank fell ill. It was cancer again, later declared incurable. But Babs did not tell Frank this, and he thought to the end of his illness that he had tuberculosis and would get better. It was probably due to smoking as Annie's was. Nearly everybody smoked in those days.

Everybody admired Babs at the time. She kept the house neat as usual, always with flowers in the hall. And she arranged as normal a life for Frank as possible, getting him up each morning, putting the television on for him and encouraging friends to sit with him. She kept herself well-dressed and cheerful, cooked and talked to friends.

Only once I saw her in despair. I called to enquire one morning and found her in her dressing-gown, her usually neat hair wild and her eyes red-rimmed. She looked about eighty. Frank was still upstairs but she was careful to speak softly lest he should hear. "Frank's been coughing all night. I haven't had a wink of sleep." But she added hastily, "I'll be all right. I've got people coming round."

Yet even in those hard days she continued her anger with Tom. "He hasn't been near us. You'd have thought that he would have just called in to enquire. Frank would have been glad of him in the after-

98

noons. All sorts of people are coming in to sit with him. But no sign of Tom."

I never knew the rights of it. Did Tom know that she was angry and so keep away? Or did he just not realise that he was expected to call? When I saw him next over the hedge I said that Babs was wondering where he was. Then he said innocently, "I haven't been because I didn't want to trouble her."

Whether he went after that I never knew. Probably not, for Babs's ordeal was cut short. One morning she had got Frank down to their back room for breakfast when he suddenly fell and became unconscious. "He never spoke again," she said. He had had a stroke on top of the cancer and died in a few hours.

Babs was an admirable widow, and her family and friends helped. Indeed at the beginning they helped almost too much. She said, a few days after the funeral, "People keep on asking me out, but I wish they wouldn't. I'd rather be quiet at home."

But she adapted. She put a large photograph of Frank in the front room and left the door open so that when people called they could see it. She talked of his life, and I heard for the first time that he had been a poor boy brought up in a "home", but after they had met he was given a job at the family works. Yet she had always treated him like royalty.

They had talked of death and what the surviving partner should do, and had decided that it would be best to stay in Redbury. Over finances she consulted the old bank at her former village. The manager advised her to put her money into more profitable investments, but she would not. "Frank made the arrangements, and what was good enough for him is good enough for me."

Before Frank retired she had been doing a part-time job mending linen with three other women at a local hospital. As usual she found them "lovely", but she had given the job up to be with Frank in his retirement. Now she had the day to herself, and she kept her old habit of standing at her gate and talking to friends as they went by to the shops.

She made friends with a schoolboy who went past each day and gave him sweets and met his mother. But she was, of course, lonely. I called one winter afternoon after work, and she asked me to stay for a cup of tea. The house was warm after a cold journey from London, and there was a bright fire in her back room, with chrysanthemums in a pot on the table. We talked cheerfully about the difficulties of catering for one, and then suddenly she was plaintive. "I just have a plate of breakfast food in the morning. In the old days I always made a cooked breakfast. I would be down in the kitchen cooking and Frank would be shaving upstairs, and I'd call 'Ready' and he'd shout 'Coming in a moment.' And then he'd come down and we'd have breakfast together. It doesn't seem worth while cooking now."

But still she kept her house comfortable and saw friends. Meanwhile the winter wore away, and I did not see her as frequently. The seasons make a difference to the small homes of Redbury. They shut early in the winter but, with spring, people come out to their gardens.

I do not know what happened in those months. Was Babs's anger against Tom only part of her grief which waned with time? Did he call after all, or did they meet by chance? Whatever happened they made peace. It was natural, I suppose. They were both good people.

I went round to Babs's house one spring morning. As she opened the front door the back door opened behind her. I said, "You've got visitors. I won't stay."

But she answered carelessly, "Oh it's all right. It's only Tom."

*Tom?* The dolt, the oaf? Yet she spoke lightly as if he were part of her home scene. It was like going back ten years.

The signs of peace continued. On another morning when I visited Babs the television was muttering from the back room. And again Babs said in the same careless tone, "It's only Tom."

Then I began to hear them from my bedroom window in the morning between eight and nine. They would issue from their back doors and meet by the gate in the fence. Babs would say, "And how are you this morning?" Then they would have a brief conversation about the weather or the day ahead or some bit of news, and then Babs would say, "See you later" and both would retire.

In the old days, punctually at eleven, Annie, Tom's wife, would call from her kitchen, "Tom, your coffee," and Tom would drop what he was doing and go in. Now again the call came, "Tom, your coffee", but it would come from the further kitchen, and in the same way Tom would stop working, and this time go through the gate in the fence.

Once I was in our garden on a summer evening and heard them on the other side of the hedge. They were wandering round Tom's terrace garden and talking quietly. Now and then Babs would stop and pick one of his flowers – either for her house or his. It was a picture of peace, and anybody would have taken them for an affectionate married couple.

Then, one morning in the late summer, I issued from my gate to go to London. At the same time the gate next door clicked and Tom came out, stout and with his respectable trilby and air of benevolence. A minute late the further gate clicked, and out came Babs, neat and beaming as usual, with her hair tidily waved and shining spectacles.

She stopped to talk while Tom strolled on to the bus-stop. "Tom's taking me on a bus trip. We're going to Ealing. Tom says there have been a lot of changes there lately. We shall look round and have a fish lunch in one of the cafés Tom likes. We'll be back for tea."

Again they were an image of a happily married pair, she vivacious and he slow and benevolent. I wondered sometimes if they would marry. But she was in her mid seventies and he in his early eighties, and each had a comfortable home and they could see one another as often as they liked. So there seemed no need.

But the companionship gave Babs a pleasant end to her life. The months passed and they continued to greet one another in the morning and go out together. However, it was not Tom but a woman friend who was with Babs one morning when she had a heart attack. This was probably fortunate as Tom would not have known what to do. The friend called an ambulance, but Babs had the strength to walk to her gate to get in.

Tom had never used a telephone. So he got up early next day and took buses to the hospital, arriving at eight o'clock. But he was too late. Babs had died ten minutes before.

Then, as usual, Tom was put aside, and Babs's family did all the business, and arranged for the funeral and for the house to be cleared and sold.

Tom returned to his dumb solitary life, but at least he had had some happy times. He behaved as after his wife's death, saying little, but one morning as he greeted me over the hedge he cried out, "Oh I do miss that woman."

# CHAPTER 14
## War Memories. Tom's Secrets.

Through the century, to many older peoples war experiences have been the sharpest memories of their lives. Mention bombs and civilians will claim that they had more raids in their areas than anywhere else. Ex-Servicemen rejoice in anniversary parades and trips to old battlefields. The years have brought a softening of memories and desire to talk with a little boasting. Even Tom Green, who kept his war experience secret, called his house "Hazebrouck", the small place on the French-Belgian borders where he killed his friend.

Tom, who lived next door, could illustrate several trends of the century, but was generally silent about himself. With a square bald head and red cheeks, he said little to us for many years except "good morning" over the hedge. I did not hear his life story until in his mid eighties he was confined at home with a broken leg.

He seemed a very ordinary old man, but his trade was not ordinary. He was a sign-writer for the local Council. I thought at first that this must be a distinguished occupation, but it turned out to be a fairly humble job – using a stencil to paint signs and lines in the streets and I suppose to paint names. He told me one evening that he had been painting footsteps all day. Pedestrian crossings had come in. The Council had fixed its first crossings, and Tom had been painting a crowd of white footsteps leading to crossings in the road so that people would be encouraged to use them.

His gardening too was unusual. In his narrow back strip leading downhill he made terraces. At the top were pots round the kitchen doorstep, a patch of grass, a small flower border and a magnificent pyrus japonica, with flowers of soft brick red, trained to stretch across the garden as a shield. A small path led down to the next terrace, a lawn with a flower border, and then to a vegetable bed flanked by currant bushes. At the bottom, where our back alley ran, were a small green shed, a fence and a gate.

Tom spent much time in his garden, cutting his privet hedges and in an amateur way hacking at his trees. He often trimmed my side of the hedge and sometimes gave me plants, but he was an unlearned gardener. He called the red heuchera in his front garden "grass" and asked me for the name of his campanulas. When I found out that it was "globosa", he said he could not pronounce it.

As one of the old countryside dwellers he loved bonfires and had an old pierced iron bucket at the end of his garden where he used to burn household refuse as well as garden rubbish. In the prevailing west wind great gusts of smoke would come rolling in at our windows, and sometimes we had to tell him that we were being choked. Tom would obligingly put his fire out, but there was a certain slowness of understanding in him and he would be fire-making again the next day. I would remark loudly that I hated bonfires, but it made no difference, and I was thankful when regulations came in to ban bonfires in the day. Tom got muddled about the hours in which they were allowed. and stopped having them altogether.

As my boys grew up he began to talk to them a little, and when they were away he talked a little more to me. One morning after the usual greeting, he suddenly said, "You see, I killed a man." It was in the First World War, but not a German but his friend. He had given his house the name of the place in the trenches where the accident had happened.

It was an accident, but Tom seemed to brood on it as if it were a crime. "Don't tell anybody," he said to me, and I promised I would not and kept my word for years. Then something my boys said showed that they knew the secret too. He had told them of the "murder" years before but also asked for silence. He seemed like the Ancient Mariner, moved from time to time to confess his crime. How many people heard of Tom's secret I did not know. Probably few as he lived a retired life.

From that time he talked a little more.

Tom's father was a smart groom working for a rich businessman in the genteel village of Esher. The groom drove his master each morning to his office at Richmond and returned to fetch him in the late afternoon. Tom always addressed me as "Madam", and I think that stemmed from his youth. So too probably did his rather wooden slow comprehension. His father wore a smart uniform, but he was a brute. He had been beaten by his father, and proceeded to beat his own boys. They were not allowed to speak at meals, and he hit them if they did. One of the things I found out about working-class people in Redbury has been that many of them had unhappy childhoods with tyrannical and often drunk fathers.

Tom, in the manner of the day, was sent out, while he was still at school, to deliver parcels and earn a few shillings a week. He worked for a chemist, delivering medicines early in the morning before he went to school. In winter he would return with "frozen" hands, and his mother, who was kind, would warm them by tucking them into her armpits.

At fourteen when he left school he left home too. The South Western Railway had a coal depot at Woking, and engines had to be cleared of ashes and then refuelled from the piles of coal by the line. The boy shovelling coal was on the lowest rung of a ladder that led up to engine-driver – Tom's ambition. His wages were very low but he found a room at Woking so that he could escape from his hated home.

Tom was too young to join the Army when the Great War broke out. But crowds of young men were volunteering, not from a sense of duty but because they wanted to escape from tedious jobs. Tom waited till he was seventeen and then volunteered saying that he was eighteen. After the heavy loss of life in the first years of the war the authorities did not enquire much about ages, and Tom was accepted, trained and in a short time was in the trenches.

More than sixty years later he told me his story without complaint – with stolid matter-of-factness. It was probably in the last year of the war that Tom, aged eighteen or nineteen, killed his mate. He had put down his gun for a minute, and somebody picked it up and charged it. He was never very perceptive and he did not know, and when he took it again it went off and killed his friend.

It was a brutal period. Tom was marched many miles behind the lines, tried by a military court and condemned to be shot. But his sentence was commuted to a hard punishment. He was to stay in the trenches for a year without leave and have a diet of bread and water. His pay, which had been going home to his mother, was stopped.

But Tom told the story without complaint. At the time rations in the trenches were so bad that a diet of bread and water made little difference. And the war ended before his sentence was finished and the punishment was abandoned.

In his cold little back room, Tom brought out faded photographs and charts. He was proud of these relics. One torn strip of paper bore a thick black line, cross-marked, and a list of names. This recorded his unit's hundred-mile march.

The group was sent after the war to occupy a country area of Germany. It marched east through Rhine country, but Tom did not remember much about the hundred miles except one incident. They were crossing a bridge in Germany, and a line of women was watching from the side. As Tom passed a woman stepped forward and spat in his face. There was nothing he could do about it; just wipe his face and march on.

But the people of the rural area where they eventually camped were not hostile. The farmer gave them milk, and Tom could still bring out a few rusty German words. The chief trouble about the camp was that there was nothing to do except self-maintenance.

Hearing this bit of war history, I suggested that Tom should record it. The Imperial War Museum in London had a tape department that preserved stories of ordinary soldiers. Tom protested, but in the end let me telephone the museum. It sent him a leaflet in thick Civil Service language which he did not understand. I had a struggle to make him consent to an interview – and then no-one came.

After a year Tom's unit returned to England and demobilisation, but he did not go back to the railway. In the camp he had gained a reputation for drawing, probably as a leisure hobby, and a mate asked him to design a poster for a cinema. A local counsellor saw it, and Tom was invited to become a Council sign-writer. It was typical that he stayed there till retirement.

I never heard how Tom met his wife Annie. She was a maid at the near-by Hampton Court Palace, working in one of the grace-and-favour apartments, and later told us that it was running with mice. He must have felt sympathy, for her family, he said, had been very cruel to her – did not want her and sent her away to service when she left school. Annie never mentioned her family, and presumably she had lost touch with them.

It was a long time before I heard of Tom's other secret, though there had been hints in his war story. One morning we met at the bottom of the garden, and on an impulse he said, "Come and see my shed."

He had run a cable down from his kitchen, and sometimes we would see a glow from the shed in the evening, but I had thought it was only a place for tools. All over the estate there were wooden shacks and sheds where men of the small houses did carpentry or car jobs. Tom beckoned me, and I went through the bottom gate on the alley. He opened the shed door and I had a surprise. The shed was a small studio with a large dim window at the further end and a fixed table below it. On the table were scattered papers and some kind of painting. Round the shed sides were high shelves holding brushes, tubes of paint and pots. An easel stood in a corner.

I went across to the table. The painting in oils on paper was of a village scene – a curve of picturesque old buildings, half-timbered and gabled, facing a village green. The complicated perspective seemed to have been well managed. The colours were bright, flat and naive.

"Where is it?" I asked Tom.

"Don't know," he said.

By the painting was a coloured postcard, a small version of the scene. Tom somehow had learnt how to enlarge subjects by squaring up the paper. He said, "I do them for neighbours."

He told me that in his spare time he enlarged postcard views and sold his paintings to neighbours for ten shillings each. I asked him why he did not paint directly from nature, and he said he did. He would go out on his bicycle and sketch the countryside. A favourite spot was a stream off the road under Box Hill.

This had been his hobby through the years, and it had been a comfort to him. After Annie's death I asked him why he did not continue it as a consolation, but he said, "I haven't the heart."

After his own death, when I was helping to clear up the house, I noticed some of his work framed on the walls. In the front room were two garden scenes with bright red brick houses and in one a small doll-like figure in a porch. In the foreground were incredibly bright riots of flowers. The paintings were naive but it was astonishing that this wooden man should have painted them at all.

In the back room, on each side of the hearth, hung a portrait – a stiff middle-aged figure down to the waist. They, too, were naive and untaught, but they were real people, not beautified.

In clearing up, a cousin and I found a big rusty key and went down and unlocked the shed. It was a scene of desolation, spiders' webs on the window and walls, dust everywhere and the brushes and tubes of paint on the shelves so dried that they were of no use. The only thing worth saving was the easel in the corner. We took it up to the house, and some of a previously unknown family, who had appeared in Tom's last illness, carried if off with the paintings and the fine model ship in the back room. "Uncle Tom", I heard, had had the reputation of an artist.

Tom's death was caused by two modern factors – road traffic and smoking. One winter afternoon he returned from one of his bus-rides and got off at his usual stop. To reach his house he had to cross the double-lane road, and for some unknown reason he decided to cross in front of the bus which was still stationary. A van was passing outside it and caught him and tossed him towards the central reservation. He lay with a bleeding head, and a crowd collected. Somebody called an ambulance.

Tom did not want to go to hospital. He begged to be taken home. But he was obviously hurt, and the ambulance carried him away. I was not there, but when later I returned from work I had a telephone call from the hospital. Tom was asking to come home and had given my name as a neighbour. They were providing supper and then he would be sent back. Would I go in and see that he was all right?

When I heard the ambulance I went in. It was a cold night, and Tom, with a great white fluff of dressing on his bald head, was sitting by a miserably small gas fire, and the room was ill-lighted and dreary. But he said he had had supper and did not want anything. So I said I would look in in the morning.

So began my visits, generally twice a day. Tom began by being reserved, but gradually talked about his life. He saw almost nobody else and was in pain and lonely. I did his shopping, the two chief necessities being tobacco for rolling cigarettes and whiskey for half a glass in the evening. Then I got one or two neighbours to cook him dinners while I was away in London, and this broke the day for him. Finally I arranged "Meals on Wheels", and he said that the food was good but the lady stopped for only a moment.

His loneliness was a great problem. Once a Jehovah's witness called and Tom asked him in for a conversation. He sold Tom a crude magazine printed in Chicago. Tom was not at all interested, and passed it on to me.

Then a German sister-in-law appeared and helped. Both of us were concerned at Tom's condition. The doctor came once, found the wound on his head better and removed the white fluff, but did not come again. Meanwhile Tom constantly complained of his legs. They both hurt him and he could hardly get upstairs. We suggested that he should keep them up, but he had to move about to look after himself.

Looking back I think I was wrong not to call the doctor in again. But Tom was reserved and one does not want to interfere. But I went in one frosty morning to find the curtains still drawn and the house in darkness. There was no sign of Tom, but from above came the sound of stertorous breathing. I went up to find him in his big double bed, with covers over his face and the terrible hoarse breaths. They sounded as if they might stop at any moment, and now and again he groaned. He seemed only half conscious. I could only say, "I'll fetch the doctor".

But the summons took four telephone calls and two hours. The receptionist told me to "bring Mr Green into the surgery", and when I said that this was impossible she said that the doctor was busy. It was, of course, the time of year for large surgeries. Finally she promised that the doctor would come – and he did not. I hovered between the two houses, afraid to leave Tom but also afraid to be out of call of my telephone. The frosty gardens seemed warmer than Tom's dim house.

A car drew up at last, and the ancient doctor appeared. It was a moment of unutterable relief. He said that Tom had a chest infection and sent me running to the chemist for a string of prescriptions. But when I returned I found that he had changed his mind, and was sending Tom back to hospital. I had to return the remedies to the chemist, but I was glad. Somebody else was taking responsibility.

The ambulance came quite soon. The ambulance men were, as

usual, cheerful and kind. I thanked heaven.

Tom's return to hospital caused some indignation. "Shameful," a sister said. He was X-rayed again, and it was found that one of his legs had been broken all the time while the other one was lacerated. So for weeks he had been in severe pain. I was told that the doctor who had first seen him had some disagreement with the X-ray department and no proper X-ray had been done. The sister said she was disgusted.

But now everything was going to be all right. A skin graft would be done, and a series of operations would be necessary. But this would be no bad thing, as it would keep Tom in the warm hospital during the cold weather. He was installed at the end of a long ward, with the usual locker and chair beside his bed. His chest infection was said to be clearing up.

When I next saw him he was sitting in his chair and seemed alert. It was marvellously warm, and he had had a little talk with the man in the next bed. He asked me for a coat and gave detailed instructions on how to find it, and told me take home a pot of chrysanthemums that somebody had given him and put it in his window.

But at the next visit he was lying in bed and saying little. And the next day he was in bed with the covers over his head. He was not eating properly, and the leg operations were postponed.

And so a decline set it. He was eighty-six and used to a solitary life, but I thought I knew the chief malaise. He had been smoking since the age of fifteen. Indeed one friend had pointed to him and said, "Look at Tom. There can't be anything wrong with smoking." While I had shopped for him I had noticed his dependence on tobacco and whiskey. But he could not smoke in the hospital ward.

Hospitals generally answer enquiries with "Comfortable", and Tom was "comfortable" at first. But there came a morning when a nurse said he was "not too well." A few hours later the telephone rang and I was told that he had died. He had been in hospital only ten days. It was perhaps best. His women had gone and he had not much to live for.

A small flurry followed Tom's death. A branch of his family who had not troubled about him in his heyday, wanted to know how he had left his money. Fortunately – and surprisingly for Tom – he had left a will. Two rival factions were each disappointed.

Then one group thought the hospital should be sued for negligence over Tom's legs. We had a session in the Guildhall, with the coroner, a barrister, the van-driver who had run him down and people who had looked after him. The session lasted for more than an hour but in the end the family decided that a law-suit would be too expensive.

The family cleared the house and put it on the market.

As spring came the terrace garden was covered with weeds. The grass grew up and became straw and fell over, and the currant bushes were matted with convolvulus. Then a new family came in and swept it all away.

Tom had lived such a retired life that few people had memories of him. But some months after his death the Imperial War Museum rang me up. His papers had gone astray but now had been found, and an interviewer would be pleased to come from London and talk to him.

I replied. "Too late."

## CHAPTER 15
### *Fish History. Jim Who Escaped.*

I have never seen a history of fish in the twentieth century, and yet there is much to say. There have been changes in our food and food habits, shopping and environment, and fewer fine young men like Bernard and Jim stand by marble slabs covered with fish corpses wafting sour odours down the street.

At the beginning of the century fish was a constant and unquestioned article of diet, connected with religion and Friday fasting. The nation was proud of its fishing villages, and artistic colonies painted them. Familiar poets such as Tennyson and Kingsley had written about them, always ennobled by death and the perils of the sea. The fish were always there with brave men to bring them to us.

But at the end of the century we have learned uncomfortable facts. Seas polluted by industry, over-fishing, dwindling fish stocks, fishing quarrels between nations make daily news. Television has complicated matters further by showing under-sea views of beautiful fish and fish that seem friendly, awaking doubts about killing them. For those who still consume them the market has been taken over by refrigeration and packaging, and no longer does every town have a fishmonger's slab with its freshly-caught corpses.

As a vegetarian I should have been able to leave fish consumption alone, but I was involved by one thing. I kept cats. Soon after the war there were not yet cat-tins with large-eyed wistful pets on the wrappers, and one of our main food resources was "pussies' pieces" – the slimy bits that remained when the fishmonger had trimmed his wares. My need for the bony "ears" and "wings" led me, inwardly protesting, to smelly slabs but also to good-hearted talkative women and two courteous young men. I was glad, though, that in the end Jim escaped.

When I began to buy pussies' pieces there were fish shops all over the place, and we had one early on our new estate. It was at a windy corner and typical of the period with an open front and a sloping marble slab adorned with dead monsters, red slices, sprigs of parsley and small melting pieces of ice. In summer countless flies and wasps hovered and crawled over it. I had not known before that wasps loved fish.

The shop was owned by a burly jokey man named Trevor, but more often in charge was the young slim Bernard. Bernard was always pleasant, but his chief asset was a passion for writing notices – in curly lettering and coloured chalks, mainly purple and pink.

The persuasive notices were propped up among the fish. Most were intelligible – "Come on Mum. Here's a bargain" or "Look! A real treat!" But I never did understand one notice which ran "Cheap's dear. Dear's cheap". I suppose it was an injunction to spend money.

The fish-shop continued for a year or two, but then packaging began and Fridays were less fish days. Trade fell off, and Trevor tried to revive it by also selling fried fish and chips. But flats had been built above Trevor's line of shops, and the occupants objected to the smoke and smell. So Trevor departed and an innocuous greengrocery followed the fish-slab. For a time we had to look elsewhere for cat food. I hoped Bernard would prosper.

"Do you know," said a man whom I met in the road, "that a fish van comes up here every Friday morning?" People seemed aware that I kept cats even when I did not know the kindly passers-by. "Quite a queue lines up at nine," the man said.

So I thought that I had better join it. It consisted nearly all of women, who began to come early to be in front of the queue. Punctually at 9.30 a white van drew up in a space in front of the shops, and out jumped another good-looking man with a very white overall. He let down the flap at the back of the van, and spent a few minutes arranging his fish on it. Then he turned to the queue and lent his ear to the first customer.

I heard that he had a partner with a shop about two miles away. The partner sold fish from the shop while Jim took his van round the neighbourhood – to a different site each day of the week. Apparently we were the most rewarding queue, perhaps because our day was Friday. The partners must have prospered, for they went off to the West Indies, Majorca and other popular overseas spots for a fortnight's holiday in summer. But Jim in his agreeable way gave us good notice of his coming absence.

On usual Fridays the queue stretched away beside the main road – standing patiently and sometimes shivering while traffic whirred by. "It's like Waterloo," the woman in front of me declared. She meant the London terminus with its then noisy trains.

The history of the twentieth century might include the history of queues. Before, I suppose, many people were too poor to compete for goods, but the Second World War generally cured that and made queuing a way of life. Queues are often cold and a waste of time but one gets to know one's fellows.

Sometimes the fish queue stood in stolid silence, huddled in an east wind. But it took only a cheerful middle-aged housewife to get conversation going. Often it began with comments on the weather and then went on to life generally – our own life. We did not broach politics or world events.

It was strange how we changed our attitudes. Crawling along towards Jim we were immersed in the queue, part of a group of anonymous loquacious housewives. But after we had reached Jim, got what we wanted and turned away, we became an individual again, looking back with scornful pity on the shabby file still chained there.

The talk was often complaints, laments for "the good old days". In the good old days we had real food, not all this made-up stuff, and we cooked our own meals according to the laws of nature. Young people now were idle and wanted all this frozen stuff. "Now my daughter-in-law..." One woman said with great authority, "Modern times are all right but modern people aren't." It sounded profound, and there was a murmur of agreement.

In spite of these laments the ladies liked to boast about their up-to-date equipment. First it was the vacuum cleaners, television, fridges and washing machines, and later freezers and double glazing. The acquisitions were not only useful but made their owners feel superior.

Our new estate had drawn people from many areas, and birth-places gave another reason for boasting. There was always something worth complacency. "I come from Yorkshire," said a woman on a very cold morning. "It's *much* colder than here. Now my mother had a fish-shop and her hands got *frozen*. But I will say this for her. She never took to drinking to warm herself up. No. She only laced her tea with whiskey." We murmured respectfully at this moral victory.

I was surprised at one response. A speaker said emphatically, "I *hate* housework," and all around came cries of "And so do I. And so do I." Had women, the homemakers, hated housework through the centuries and been in a prison of convention? In my mind's eye I saw a long trail of women pretending to love the homes they hated. Thank God now for vacuum cleaners.

But the best queue talks were about stupid neighbours. They, more than anything, made us feel superior. "Now my neighbour has left her husband and lives with a lover further down the road. Two young children too. Now wouldn't you think she'd take some notice of her own children? But she never does though she's only a few doors away. He'd had to get in the grandmother to look after them."

"Oh. Oh what a shame!"

The longest story to make us feel superior was about that subject that excites many passions – smoking. A bright little woman descended from a car and said "Good morning" as she stood at the back of the queue. One could tell that she would cheer us up.

"He's a good sort to bring me down," she said. "I live two miles away. But it isn't for myself I've come. The woman who lives next door wants some fish."

So she was charitable, was she? We warmed to her.

"She's got a hospital appointment," the little woman said. "As a matter of fact she's killing herself." More people turned their heads.

"Smoking. She's been smoking since the age of fifteen. The hospital says she must give it up, but I bet you that when she gets home this morning she'll take out a fag."

It was a long story. We almost forgot Jim. "The whole family smokes. Smoking killed her husband seven years ago. Then she had to get a job. She went to the Government offices up the road. But she smoked more than ever."

"I know," a voice chimed in. "They smoke like chimneys up there."

"She had to have a breast operation three years ago. Now it's her lungs, and she's losing weight. She's wasted thousands and thousands of pounds, and now she's fifty-seven. 'I'm fifty-seven', she says. 'And what have I had out of life?' She won't see that it's her fault."

"Any children?" somebody asked.

"She's got a daughter."

"Warned by her mother, I expect," somebody said.

"Now that's a funny thing," the little woman went on. "The daughter smokes as much as the mother. Her house is full of smoke. She's got three children, and they'll be at it soon, I shouldn't wonder."

"Doesn't she know she's being silly?"

"Doesn't seem to. Both she and her mother are brainy women, and they know that smoking kills people. But they say they're different from everybody else, and it won't hurt them. It's no good talking to them."

She stopped as we moved forward. We should have felt saddened, but what we mainly felt was self-congratulation and superiority. We are born with this desire to be better then other people.

But then Jim was bending to hear my order, and the queue faded away.

"Pussies' pieces, please, as usual."

We all loved Jim. He was tall and slim, with red-brown hair and that dazzling white overall, and he was probably still in his twenties. His manners were unfailingly kind, and there was a romantic solitude about him as he arrived punctually each week from somewhere unknown. One woman told me that he was separated from a wife, but we heard nothing about it. As he bent quietly to hear our wants he reminded me of a father confessor holding secret conversations. He did not seem to object that I wanted only pussies' pieces.

I asked him once why he had become a fishmonger. He said that mates of his had been involved in the fish trade at Hull, and he had gone into business with them. He did not seem to think that he might be doing something better.

Once or twice I had to miss the queue because of hospital appointments. I told him beforehand, and he offered at once to leave the pussies' pieces on my doorstep at the end of the morning. "You can pay the week after." Sure enough, when I returned I found a bulky slimy plastic bag by the door.

He always stayed till twelve-thirty after the queue had melted away – to oblige any late-comers. He would stand peacefully reading a newspaper with the flap still down. Once I came late and found him dealing with a small strange woman who seemed deaf and dumb. She was mouthing and pointing, and he was patiently lifting one fish after another for her decision. At last she nodded, and he wrapped up the fish and showed her the price. There seemed no difficulty. When she had gone I said, "I suppose you know her."

"Never seen her before," he said.

After a year or so there came splendid news. Jim was separating from his partner with the shop and taking a shop of his own. By chance the shop behind his van site had just fallen vacant, and Jim was to rent it.

What a blessing! No more queues in the east wind. We could go down when we liked. And the shop had its fish-slab inside so that we should be sheltered from the weather for our pleasant trading.

The shop opened. It was not as crowded as I had expected, but of course it had all day to do business. There was a counter between Jim and the customer so that he seemed more remote. With him was a quiet elderly man who he said was his father. Sometimes the elderly man was in the shop alone.

It went on for several months, but trade did not increase. In those days people still cooked a Sunday joint and ate it cold for several days afterwards. Fish was not wanted till the middle of the week, and also recently prices had gone up. Jim was selling no more than he had sold from his van, and the shop rent was high.

We were not surprised when he announced that the shop was closing. It was not a staggering blow, for the grocery stores were by this time selling packed frozen fish and tins of cat food. But I was sorry for Jim. And he seemed to have lost touch with us.

But once before the shop closed I did ask him about his future. He said he had taken another shop about four miles away in a more urban area.

"There will be more people there wanting fish," I said.

He said, "I'm not selling fish any more."

"What then?"

"It's a flower shop."

What a delightful change! Roses instead of haddock. The scent of daffodils instead of sweating coley. No need to worry about week-end joints. Customers concerned not with their stomachs but with loving messages.

"How splendid!" And I hope it was.

But Jim did not come back; so I never heard.

# The World of Eccentrics. Mrs Pretty's Pets.

At the end of the century we are being entertained by murder, drug addiction, robbery, cheating and crooked sex. We like them, of course, or newspapers and television would not deal them out in such quantities. There is something in human nature that enjoys being shocked by wickedness. But it is a fantasy world. The criminals decked out with luscious details for our amusement are in the minority. Most of us, in the developed western world anyhow, may be mean, selfish and stupid, but we generally obey regulations. Some people stand out by their goodness or intelligence. And then there are the eccentrics who have their own interests and let the ordinary world go by.

Mrs Jessie Pretty could not have told you what the Moors murders were, but she knew a needy cat when she saw one.

When I met Mrs Pretty down at the shops she was already old with very white hair, very blue eyes, pink cheeks and hobbling feet. There was something very innocent and respectable about her, and she made odd remarks and was, in a way, outside the contemporary world. "Poor" cats and dogs lapped her round.

It is easy to talk to people down at the shops. You see the same faces day after day, and the shops themselves are in two lines separated by a rushing road crossed by pedestrian crossings and lights. So you stop a good deal and generally find a neighbour beside you. One day you smile; the next comment on the weather; and the next are talking of families and operations.

You gossip before you know people's histories, and it was some time before I learned Mrs Pretty's story. She came of a family which acted as servants and gardeners to aristocratic houses and so had learned polite manners. She had married a countryman, a worker on one of the Redbury farms in the first half of the century, and had been surrounded by animals and fields. The first disturbance of the countryside came in the 1930s when a single-track bypass was built to cut across the fields. It has since become one of London's main outlets, but at first it was an irritation only to local inhabitants. It ran across the Prettys' farm fields, and a boy used to step out and hold up traffic so that the cows could cross to be milked.

The district changed, but the Prettys stayed. When "Dad" retired they settled on a new estate. The Council by this time had had experience of building estates, and this one was among the most pleasant of the area. It was built on the gardens of an old large house that stood beside but above the main road, and was retired and reached by a grass slope. Winding small roads curled between grassy frontages. Large old trees were left, and the small houses were given good gardens. Here the Prettys settled, perched above the busy road which later produced victims which Mrs Pretty tended. A married son settled beside them so that there was a good plot of land behind.

"Dad", who was used to animals, had every kind of pet including rabbits in cages all round the gardens. He also grew roses, dahlias and other summer flowers so successfully that "you couldn't see an inch of bare earth", according to his son. He won prizes in Council garden competitions, and crowds of people came to see and admire.

But when I first met Mrs Pretty "Dad" was dying of dropsy. It was a long illness and she gave me many details. You would think they were sickening – and they were – but she described them with such an innocent detachment that I did not mind. She did not complain, but when he at last died she had grown thinner. After that she talked little of family matters. It was all dogs, cats and pets.

When I next met her she reported that her bantams were good layers. "I got them for Dad, but they take a lot of looking after."

"You're not going to have them killed?"

"No dear, of course not. You know me."

I said I supposed the eggs were very small.

"Oh no, dear," she asserted. "Mine are very big bantams."

Can one have big bantams? It sounded a contradiction in terms. But of course she knew more about poultry than I did.

I came to expect odd remarks that might have made sense or might not. Once when, like everybody else, we were complaining of the cost of living, she dismissed the problem with, "Oh well, my dear, we shall all have to live together." *All?* Did she mean the neighbours, the borough or the nation? At least it showed friendliness to humanity.

But her other friendliness was to dogs and cats. A doctor had a surgery beside the Prettys' houses, and she used to clean his rooms. He went away for a holiday and left his two dogs in her keeping, and when he returned he said he was tired of them. So would she keep them? She did for the rest of their lives.

She had a dog of her own, and met me one day to say in her placid way that it too had gone. "I've had to have my poor Jack Russell done in. He had something wrong with his liver. So I gets the vet and he comes with a nurse. The vet said he couldn't do nothing. So first they gives him an injection and then another injection in a vein. Then they wraps him up nicely and takes him away. The vet says he'll examine him when they gets back. 'Make sure he's dead,' I says.

She was still seeing the best in everything. "They only charged me five pounds. I thought that was good, considering the nurse came too. The dog was twelve or thirteen so he didn't do so bad."

I once asked Mrs Pretty, when she was about ninety, if she had stopped keeping pets. She thought a moment. "Well dear. I have the bantams and the mynah bird I took when Daphne's father died. Daphne's my daughter-in-law. I had the old man's dog too, but he's gone. The mynah bird's all right though. He makes me laugh.

"Then there's Sam of course. Sam's a white cat belonging to a young couple near me. They've got two dogs; so Sam comes to me. They say they're pleased I take him. It gives the cat a rest from the dogs.

"This morning at 7.30 as usual, when I comes down to make a cup of tea, in he walks. They turn him out at night; so he was hungry. I opens him a tin, and then he wants to sit on my lap. 'But I can't,' I says. 'I'm in my dressing gown'. So I finds a nice little blanket, and I spreads it on a chair, and Sam gets on it and goes to sleep – sleeps till half-past eleven. He comes every day, and I have tit-bits for him."

Many of Mrs Pretty's services were for animals owned by somebody else or nobody. Every evening she took food to a colony of escaped feral cats inhabiting a bit of open ground a little way away. Her son told me that on one evening when rain was pouring down her family begged her not to go. But she went all the same and returned wet to the skin.

Then there were the cats killed on the road. A succession of these occurred as the neighbourhood was full of pets, and the gardens had only low fences so that it was impossible to keep animals in. One morning Mrs Pretty hurried up to me in the street and took my arm. A cat had been killed on the road but in its death throes had run up a drive. The owner of the drive had removed it and laid it on the pavement. This made Mrs Pretty angry. "Didn't care at all for the poor thing. Treated it like rubbish."

But she cared. "Come and see if it's one of yours," she said to me.

I had just checked my cats but I could not suppress a shiver. Cats are adepts at suddenly escaping and getting killed. Mrs Pretty led me along the road, and there at the foot of the drive was a comely little tortoiseshell.

"Not mine," I said thankfully.

But Mrs Pretty was not giving up the quest. "Well, dear, if it's not yours I shall just have to go on enquiring."

I was in a hurry and left her, but the next day she boarded me again. "I've found out who owned the poor cat. Somebody said that the people at number five had a little tortoiseshell. So I goes along and asked if they've lost a cat, and, yes, they'd been searching for it all the morning. 'Is it badly hurt?', she says. I says, 'I'm afraid...' She cried like anything. Only a kitten."

But Mrs Pretty still had duties to perform. "I looked after the poor thing. I wrapped a nice bit of nylon curtain round it and then puts it in a nice plastic bag. Then I takes it along to the woman. A neighbour comes to the door. She was in there comforting them. They were crying like as if it was one of them that had died."

Through such services Mrs Pretty was known to many neighbours, even newcomers. When I met her once she asked me, "Did you hear about those people in the big house – the one where the old lady died? Well, they brought three cats, but one has just been run over. A most peculiar cat, nearly all white but with black markings. A shame though. It was lying in the road. Yes, quite dead."

But not quite all the stories were of disasters. Once we met in the Post Office, a roomy building in those days and a place for conversation. She was beaming and excited. "I just heard from my cousins in London. They have a little shop, you see. Have had it for years. An old lady comes in, you see, a poor old thing, they think, with nothing much to live on. So they're good to her; let her have things cheap. So she comes back and keeps coming for years. But they never know anything about her except that she's old and on her own. But now, now, what a surprise! They've had a letter. She's died but she wasn't poor after all. She's left them two bungalows. *Two.* So they can live in one and sell the other."

Mrs Pretty was flushed and triumphant, but this was not quite the end of the story. "And, do you know?, she's left them her cat too."

But Mrs Pretty herself did not always have luck. One day a neighbour told me that she had been robbed, or would have been robbed except for a vigilant gentleman. Again it was in the Post Office. She had just collected her pension and was at the door when some young thief snatched the money and ran out into the street. A man standing near saw him and chased him. It was a long run, but in the end the man caught the thief and marched him back to the Post Office. What Mrs Pretty said to him I never heard but from her it could not have been very fierce.

When I saw her again I asked if she had been to the Police. People in Redbury are always going to the Police about petty thefts. Not that the Police do much. But Mrs Pretty was different. She always took troubles without complaint. "No dear," she said. "I think I'll stay quiet. You see there are all these gangs about. And if you annoy one somebody else may get you." The idea of a vast network of criminals lurking round us was common in the area, but her placid attitude contrasted with her indignation about the wrongs of cats.

She concerned herself with my cats as she did with all the others. One morning, returning from shopping, I came across her hobbling along my side of the road. This was unusual as she had difficulty in dodging the traffic, but she said she was visiting a neighbour. Then came the invariable question, "And how many cats have you got now?"

"Good gracious," I said. "You've reminded me. One of my cats went out with me, and it hasn't come back."

This had been the multi-coloured Sandstorm who liked the public. She would sit on the front gate and parade along the fence, inviting passers-by to stroke her – and they generally did. She also liked to trot beside me when I went down to the shops, but she stopped half way, retired into an opening and joined me when I returned. But that

121

morning I had forgotten to look for her.

"Would she be handsome like a Persian?" Mrs Pretty asked "The one I see sitting on your gate the other day?" Sandstorm was far from a Persian, and had a crooked orange blob on her nose and a squinting eye. But to Mrs Pretty all cats were handsome.

I went back to look for the cat, but could not find her. Then I became aware of Mrs Pretty returning, having apparently cut her visit short. "I come back to tell you I did see a cat further down lying in an entrance."

"Not hurt?" I said aghast.

"No dear, I don't think so. She moved her head."

She led me back down the road while I called and peered into gateways. In a few minutes Sandstorm emerged, sleek and undamaged, rubbing herself on a gatepost. She advanced to Mrs Pretty as she always did to strangers.

"It's a pity she comes out so much," Mrs Pretty said. "She being so handsome. You never know but she might be stolen."

A gang of cat thieves was supposed to be haunting us – kidnapping pets, murdering them, skinning them and selling their fur. I suppose there may have been cat thieves about though I never met them. In any case I hoped that Sandstorm with her blob and squint would not attract them.

Anyhow she was now safe for the moment. I picked her up, and Mrs Pretty, having done some more rescue work, skedaddled across the road to her own side.

Mrs Pretty came of a long-lived family, and she was over ninety when she fell and broke her hip. When I heard that she was in hospital I thought I had seen the last of her, but a few weeks later there she was at the shops again, a little shrunken and stooping and with a stick but still unruffled. She had had a comfortable time in hospital, she said, and doctors and nurses were wonderful. She was in no pain and could get out with "me stick". Then she began to ask about my cats.

The last I saw of her was when I was working in my front garden. I was aware of a figure peering over my gate; and there she was stooping and frail but talkative as ever. "I see you've still got your cats" and then, "I've forgotten me stick, but it don't matter. I can manage. Keep jogging on. That's what I say. Keep jogging on" and she gallantly jogged up the road.

Later she disappeared from the shops, and her son said he was doing her shopping. "But she's all right. Quite comfortable."

Finally it was, "Did you hear that Mum has died? Quite peaceful. She didn't suffer at all. Ninety-three. Good wasn't it?"

And it was almost the tone in which Mrs Pretty herself announced happy deaths of pets.

# CHAPTER 17
## *August Night.*

We talk of centuries and millennia, but of course they are only shields. They shield us from the universe in which nothing fits.

I sit at my bedroom window in the deep August night. The golden oblong windows have melted into darkness, and the neighbourhood is asleep. The taller trees in the small gardens stand out, dark black against the paler black of the sky. They are part of life, and so are the roses and the fox that steals down the alley. But they know nothing of our time measurements.

Our time measurements are ways of forgetting that we know nothing of the impulse behind the galaxies. We know certain facts, including the huge size and great number of the galaxies which seem to have no purpose. On our own earth the innumerable forms of life live only by killing one another, and the killing is completely ruthless and completely ignores the victim. The earth itself has volcanoes, tornados, floods, earthquakes to kill us, and the solar system will die in so many million years. We ourselves shall die in a few decades.

But some facts to do not fit in with this disastrous picture. We and perhaps other higher mammals have developed love, kindness, self-sacrifice and, totally against anything that could be expected, have created the arts. In contrast with almost everything else we have emotions of despair and delight. And some of us and the higher animals have extra-sensory powers, knowing things without the use of our senses. Also some of our best people have a deep feeling that all is well.

The facts must fit somehow, be we cannot see how. And the more we discover about the universe the more puzzling it becomes.

So in August nights we sit and ponder on our ignorance and at the same time feel a vague sense of exaltation.

But I too must leave the night and go to bed and dream. Dreams incidentally take a good deal of swallowing.

*The End*